CW00662243

Here, Where Death Delights

Here, Where Death Delights

A Literary Memoir

Mary Jumbelic, M.D.

Final Words Publishing

The following chapters have been previously published:
Handprints originally published as "The Boy", Tortoise and Finch, 2017, **My Father's Shadow**, Months to Years, 2022, **The Morgue**, *GFT Presents: One in Four*, GFT Press, 2017, **Scents and Sensibilities**, Prometheus Dreaming, 2021, **The Shoe**, Griffel, Issue #10, 2022, **First Interview**, *Conversation Anthology*, Unleash Press, 2022, **Flies**, *A Collection of Vignettes from Across the Globe*, Vine Leaves Literary Journal, 2017, **That Kid**, *The Power of the Pause Anthology*, Waking Up Press, 2022, **Belt Buckle**, *Light & Darkness Anthology*, Central Texas Writer's Society, 2022, **The Scream**, Matterpress, 2017, **Green Stuff**, *Mishaps and Misadventures*, Moss Piglet, Krazines, 2022, **Home**, Foliate Oak Literary Magazine, 2017, **Death as my Colleague**, *Final Acts, Death, Dying, and the Choices We Make*, Rutgers University Press, 2010, **Collapse**, Dreamers Creative Writing, 2021, **On the Way to School**, Hektoen International, 2021, **The Backpack** originally published as "The Excavation", Multiplicity, Issue #4, 2022, **Vesey Street**, Change Seven, 2022, **Dinner Hour**, Blood & Bourbon, 2022, **The Trailer**, Women on Writing, 2022, **Dead End**, The Write Launch, 2022, **The Taking Tree**, *It Was a Mistake*, Free Spirit, 2022, **Stairwell**, Jelly Bucket, 2021, **Watching Her**, Women on Writing, 2021, **The Champion**, Grapple Alley, 2021, **The Visit**, Iron City Magazine, Issue #6, 2021, **Prague**, Blood & Thunder, 2022, **Facing Demons**, Ninetenths Quarterly, 2022, **In the Kitchen**, Humans of the World, 2022, and **Pandemic** originally published as "Pandemic, the Game", The Closed Eye Open, 2021

Published by Final Words Publishing
maryjumbelic.com

Library of Congress Control # 2023911363

ISBN 979-8-9882052-0-3

Typesetting services by BOOKOW.COM

To my son, Joshua,
my constant cheerleader and counsel in equal measure.

Thank you for sharing this journey with me.

Preface

This book is true, as far as one's memory can ever be. I relied on personal journals, photo documentation, case reports and logs as well as researching facts through archived news reports, with verification of dates, time, season, and weather. The details provided adhere to the spirit of the events. Most of the names in this book have not been changed except for a few instances where I felt it appropriate to do so.

ACKNOWLEDGMENTS

It takes a lot of people to support a writer in creating a book. Thanks to the Downtown Writer's Center, YMCA, Syracuse, NY for introducing me to the art of the craft and nurturing me as I found my voice. Specific thanks to Georgia Popoff, first my mentor and then my copy and developmental editor.

I owe gratitude to the dozens of peers who critiqued individual stories in classes and workshops, and to those who spent time analyzing my entire manuscript: Dawn Penniman, Carol Decker, Jennifer Blatchley, and Joshua Safran.

To the twenty-nine digital and print literary journals that published individual pieces and grew my confidence, I am grateful. I'm even appreciative for the rejections that fueled my determination, especially those who offered words of advice and encouragement, Dan Lehman of River Teeth.

My family has given me support, attention, and material for this memoir: my husband, Marc Safran, and my three sons, Joshua, David, and Martin. They came to book readings and library lectures, and clapped enthusiastically every time I had a story published. I love you all.

The photographs were taken throughout my life; most captured by me or my husband except where another is credited in the caption. Marc has professionally restored older images and improved their quality with his expertise. I am extremely grateful to him for the professional headshot.

Thanks to Joshua Jumbles for the incredible cover design. This original illustration is a perfect representation of the book's flavor.

This project wouldn't have been possible without the expertise of Steve Passiouras from bookow.com who beautifully typeset the manuscript and rearranged it without complaint every time I requested a change. I am indebted to his tireless efforts.

I met incredible people on this journey; many appear in this book. Forensic professionals at each stage of my career guided and befriended me. I am thankful for the lessons learned and the comradery we shared, especially with my co-workers in Chicago (shout-out to Carl Jones), in Peoria (praise to the inimitable Paul Steinbach), and in Syracuse. In the latter, they are too numerous to mention but here are a few special folks—Ron Brunelli, Brian Ehret (BATO), Shane Gillen, Gloria Holland, Don Jaeger, Mo Lupia, Jacqueline O'Toole, and Catherine Unger.

Praise to all those in death investigation who work hard for the decedents, identify bodies, comfort those left behind, and never lose sight of the person on the gurney.

This book is about me and the interweaving of my personal and professional lives. My patients are an integral part of this work. I am honored to tell their stories. They have helped me tell mine.

Epigraph

Hic locus est ubi mors gaudet succurrere vitae.

This is the place where death delights to help the living.

From an inscription at Palazzo del Bo, University of Padova

Oldest surviving anatomical theater, 1594

CONTENTS

Prologue

Bright yellow, red, and blue artwork hung on my office wall. The handprints held my attention transforming from primary colors to dripping blood red. I stared at the finger-painted images, a framed Mother's Day gift from my three sons. Their hands progressed in size, just like my boys progressed in age. I shut and reopened my eyes.

The snow fell thickly, a white blur against the black outside. At 4:30 p.m. it was already dark in Syracuse. A few reports lay open on my desk next to a cup of coffee, refreshment I needed in the afternoon.

Earlier I had stood in my blue uniform jumpsuit before a small two-bedroom ranch, cream shingles with brown trim. Yellow tape that read "Crime Scene, Do Not Cross" lined the walkway. Police turned and nodded at me as I passed. The setting was muted although 10 people were about. No one spoke. Tragedy permeated the air. I showed my badge, *Medical Examiner*, to the officer at the front door.

Entering the house, I walked up the few stairs to a child's bedroom, the only sound the swooshing of the plastic booties on my feet.

"Morning, ma'am," a detective said. He pushed open the bedroom door. I followed him into the room.

Tiny, bloody handprints formed a crooked line from the floor to the wall to the door—some right-sided, some left, many distinct enough to make a fingerprint identification. A few of the 20 or so marks were less defined and smeared, the individual imprints unevenly spaced as they determinedly made a path towards the hallway.

The detective closed the door to let me see the other side. There was staining on the lower half. The brass knob was crimson from slippery attempts by the child to turn it.

My throat caught. I blew deeply out of my nose in a forceful exhale.

"Need anything, Doctor?" the detective said.

"Has this room been processed yet?" I said. Though I was responsible for the bodies, law enforcement was in charge of the scene.

In the middle of the wooden floor, between the twin bed and the door, lay a small blond child. At three years old, with a thin build, and a Dutch-boy haircut, he was a doppelgänger of my middle son, David, at that age. The little boy was on his stomach, arms outstretched, as if he had gotten tired while playing. Action figures, wood puzzles, and foam building blocks scattered around him. Except for the blood pooling around his head, the toddler could have been napping. His skin paled white but his palms and Superman pajamas were soaked red.

My gloved hands carefully turned his body over to examine the source of the bleeding, large wounds on his neck. Holding his head with my left hand, I noted that a serrated knife had been drawn against his neck with such tension it created little hatch marks from its edge along the adjacent skin. Four long incisions started near the ear and continued to the front at the Adam's apple. One had gone deep and sliced into the jugular vein.

Noting the size and shape of injuries, I explained to the detective the kind of weapon the assailant used, showing him the unique pattern. He excused himself to inform the Crime Scene Investigators (CSI) about this new information.

Inspecting the child's fingers revealed a small slice at the tip of the right index where he had tried to stop the blade. I imagined the last moments of his life—confused about the sudden pain, touching his neck with his hands.

Brushing the hair away from the little boy's forehead, a cerise swelling bloomed, from a direct hit to his face or a fall at the time of fatal collapse. Lifting the pajama shirt to get a closer look at his chest and arms revealed bruises on the tops of the shoulders and biceps where someone had forcibly held him down. The circular contusions were made by large adult-sized digits.

I envisioned the boy's terror as he bled from the nick in his vessel. His airway uninjured, he might have screamed. The abstract sound hovered at the edge of my mind. Probing gingerly, I observed the carotid artery had been spared. If this large vessel in the neck had been pierced, the resulting blood loss would have caused unconsciousness in seconds. Instead, the injured vein led to a slower exsanguination making the ink for the trail of handprints.

If the child had intended to escape the attack to find his mom, it was useless. She lay dead in the adjoining hallway, her head crushed by an ornamental rock wielded as a weapon by the same murderer. The mother was splayed on the floor, face down with arms extended toward her son's bedroom.

Blood soaked her long, brown hair and covered the wounds in the skull. Large clots formed a halo around her head. She had been dead longer than her son. I mentally arranged the timeline. The boy likely heard the fighting between his mom and the killer. How many blows did it take to silence the mom? Did the man gag her? Did she claw at him? These questions would wait until the bodies could be transported to the morgue where I would scrutinize them using surgical lights and dissecting tools.

Parent and child had been separated physically by the bedroom door but were still connected by their frantic attempt to reach one another.

The search for the killer had begun before the murders when neighbors heard a loud argument and fighting at the house. Police arrived to find the two dead victims. The lady next door had seen the estranged husband entering the home before the fight.

A dragnet ensued for the man using a picture on file from an order of protection issued earlier in the month. Officers reviewed closed circuit cameras at all gas stations and convenience stores within a five-mile radius.

Inside the small bedroom, the detective's pager buzzed. He checked the screen.

"Looks like they caught him," he said. "He bought a pack of smokes less than a mile from here."

A knock on my office door interrupted this reflection. I hadn't moved from my chair, the reports unfinished on my desk, my coffee long cold.

My secretary said, "Dr. J, we're leaving now. Don't forget to lock up."

The handprints had become artwork again. The blood was gone.

"Wait up," I said. "I'll walk out with you."

I drove home sipping cold coffee.

As I opened the back door, feet thundered toward me.

"Mommy's home!" Arms found purchase around my knees, waist, and neck, as my three young sons welcomed me back to my world.

My tears flowed freely, unrestrained by the confines of professionalism. They spilled onto my boys' hair and faces, embraces returned. I held their bodies tightly.

The panic and sadness of the slain mother and child faded into the background, but the bloody handprints, a shadow behind my boys' playfulness, remain fresh.

It is my job to bear witness and to remember. I speak for the dead.

Part I

Early Years

Death is like a Vaudeville hook
pulling me back
time and again.

My Father's Shadow

"I'm not coming home," Dad said. His sky-blue eyes, rimmed pink, showed spidery blood vessels in the surrounding white.

"No," I protested.

We sat at the gray and white speckled linoleum table in the kitchen. The chair legs scraped the floor as he pushed back and I climbed onto his lap, putting my arms around his neck. At 13, I felt awkward for this comfort, my body lanky, my mind on bell-bottoms and boys. Still, I pressed my face against his; the tang of his Aqua Velva tickled my nose. His cheek, soft and freshly shaven, rested on my forehead. My palms and armpits were sweaty as if I'd run up the 30 steps from the street to our Baltimore row house, situated at the top of an old quarry.

"Listen to me," he tried again, "I am not coming home." His voice lilted with an accent, a remnant of the Pennsylvania Slavic community where he grew up.

"Did you tell Mom?" I said.

"No, not yet" he said and gently turned my face to his. "You have to be strong for Mom. Take care of her."

The Frigidaire handle held my attention; I could not look at him. Yellow lace curtains danced at the cracked windowpane next to the back yard.

"Over here," a voice in the alley called. It sounded like my friend, Dennis, close enough that he might be talking to me.

"Coming," another kid said. They were rounding up a team for kickball, our daily after-school activity.

The clock on the counter ticked loudly. Our German Shepard pup whined behind the closed cellar door. *Scratch, scratch, scratch*—he clawed at the wood, demanding to go out romping with the boys. He yipped, rapid high-pitched sounds alternating with a lower, prolonged cry. I wanted to chorus with him in a Tarzan yell and beat my chest.

My father and I were alone in the house, except for the dog. My mother was at work. My parents alternated job shifts so I would never be unchaperoned. It was their routine; they had been doing this day to evening do-si-do since I was born. I had no siblings, grandparents, aunts, nor uncles to babysit me. In the eighth grade, I could have stayed by myself after school.

My mother had hoped for a dozen kids. After 12 years of marriage, she and my dad were blessed with one child, me. Our world was the three of us.

"Huckleberry," Dad said, hugging me tightly, thick arms wrapped around my waist. Of all the nicknames he had for me, I loved this endearment the most. It rhymed with my given name—Mary. My father enjoyed making up sobriquets for the neighborhood kids, too, old-fashioned monikers that came from a grandparent's generation and suited him at the age of 69. As the streetlights came on, parents called out Benny and Penelope and Samantha for the real Kevin, Renee, and Dana.

My father was much older than my mom. He had married in his mid-forties, saving my mother, 18 years his junior, from servitude to her adoptive family. I puzzled out this history later when I investigated my parents' opaque genealogy. I knew nothing of this at the time; they were simply my mommy and daddy.

A car horn honked three times. My father remained seated. He seemed tired, even more than the usual weariness from long hours going up and down ladders painting houses. The heart attack he had six weeks earlier at Christmas made him look different—a thinner, paler version of himself. Staying at home since then on medical orders hadn't resolved his fatigue.

"How's your leg?" I asked and got off his lap to look at the calf, the site of his most recent problem. It felt cold to the touch, like a pack of bologna from the refrigerator and as colorless as my school uniform blouse.

"Come on, walk me down to the cab," he said.

"The hospital will fix you, Daddy. They'll take that blood clot out of your leg."

"Stop it, Mary, I told you, I'm not coming home." An uncharacteristic sharpness crept in his tone. "I'm going to die."

The words slapped me. They bounced around like balls in the bingo roller on Friday nights at St. Michael's. I walked down the front stairs to the street supporting my dad as he leaned heavily on my arm. He took one step at a time, leading with his left leg, sparing the right one with the blocked blood vessel. My body felt as frigid and stiff as that leg. We descended slowly, stopping at every third riser for Dad to take a wheezy breath. Not only was his limb diseased but his insides too.

At the sidewalk, I breathed rapidly; the air thin without enough oxygen as if we were at the top of Mount Everest. My dad and I had climbed down our hill not conquering anything at all.

My father slid into the backseat of the waiting taxi. I watched him pull away, both of us waving until each was out of sight.

I no longer wanted to play kickball with my friends. I let the dog out in the yard. Waiting for my mom, I tried to convince myself that my father was being dramatic. He had a flare for the imaginary. This was like one of his tall tales—hopping trains to travel like a hobo and narrowly escaping the law, climbing out a bathroom window after a girlfriend proposed marriage, running through the woods when a bear stole his basket of berries.

Once he told me a story about a lump on his forehead. The skin mole was tan and the size of a dime, raised about 1/8 inch from the surface near his left eyebrow.

"Ran into a nasty nest of bees, trying to get me some honey," he had laughed. I pictured him stealing it, Winnie-the-Pooh style, and an angry swarm attacking him. That particular tale I believed for years.

His fictional accounts centered on the town in which he grew up in the heart of coal-mining country. We visited his childhood home every Memorial Day trekking to the highest point in the cemetery to put flowers on the graves of his parents and brothers. The family house could be seen from this vantage point nestled among identical two-story wooden buildings adjacent to a train track. There was a stone outhouse and a large coal bin in the backyard and a playground across the tracks.

"Faster, faster," I would yell to my dad as I gripped the handle of the roundabout and the world blurred to green and brown. His face became indistinguishable from the trees and hills.

My living room fogged through my tears.

By the time my mother got home, I had made a Swanson's Chicken Pot Pie for our dinner. Mom was quiet. I was too.

Dad's words clouded over. This "going to die" narrative was a yarn and I buried it in anthracite dust in my mind.

A week of winter days dragged by. Mom and I visited Dad every day at the hospital. The surgical unit where he was housed required visitors to be at least 16 years old. This necessitated costuming on my part—donning my mother's clothes, blush, and lipstick to make me look older. Pretending to be an adult gave these sojourns an air of theater.

I found comfort in the uniformed nurses, strict rules, reassuring doctors, and chemical aromas. Everyone there took good care of Daddy.

At home, I missed our daily viewing of the television show, *What's My Line.* Daddy and I tried to guess the contestants' occupation faster than the celebrity panelists.

"Teacher, teacher," I would shout.

"No, she's a secretary," Daddy would counter.

We liked to watch rebroadcasts of *You Bet Your Life*. We answered the quiz questions before the featured couple and laughed at the duck dressed like Groucho Marx that popped into the scene whenever someone said the secret word.

He and I loved puzzles and competing. We kept a tally of wins. On the day he went to the hospital I was up 2:1 that week.

My father's words of warning remained interred. Even when the surgery to remove the blood clot from his leg was canceled, the worry didn't return. Another surgery was scheduled in its place, this time to excise a mass discovered on a routine chest x-ray. The lung cancer, developed after years of working in the coal mines, inhaling paint fumes, and cigarette smoking, became the priority. My naivety fended off mortal concerns.

My dad was an inpatient for a week.

The night before the lung operation, Mom and I traveled to the hospital. My parents talked quietly as I stared out of the window at the February drizzle hitting the pavement. The Towson neighborhood was lit with streetlamps amid a moonless sky. My legs swung back and forth on the visitor's chair showing my impatience to get home. I had a lot of homework in my last semester before high school.

"Let's go," Mom said. "We have to catch the 7:15 bus." She bent down to kiss my dad on the lips and then smoothed his thick, black hair. It was one of his best features.

I hurried over to the bed and gave him a quick hug. He returned the embrace, pulling me into him. The moment stretched out. I squirmed to be free.

The next day, my mother took off work and waited at the hospital as my father underwent surgery. I went to school and afterwards walked to a friend's house down the street from where we lived. Mom planned to pick me up from there.

We girls sprawled on the floor next to a Mattel Thingmaker. The toy heated and hardened our flower and creepy-crawly plastic creations. I was making a pink and green floral pin and had decided I would give it to my mom.

The front door opened. My mother stood in the doorway, her winter coat misbuttoned, one glove on, no hat; the cold air seeped into the room. A hiss sounded in the radiator.

"Your father died," she announced. She reached to brush hair out of her eyes with a shaky hand. "He didn't feel any pain. Never even woke up from the anesthesia. The doctor said his heart couldn't take it." She shook her head as if to reckon with this insufficient explanation.

Mom's eyes were dry but puffy and red as I had seen them after an argument with my dad. Her body slid down onto the sofa. I sat down next to her. My friend closed the front door and left the room. I don't know how long we stayed there, our sides touching, the shock like a weight holding us down.

Your father died—nonsensical, just like my dad's declaration a week earlier. Surreal words that changed prophecy to reality. Daddy knew he wouldn't survive the operation. He tried to tell me; I hadn't understood.

Four days later, I sat in the front pew at the funeral dressed in a black shift and chapel veil, bought for this occasion. I felt separated from everyone else in the church as if I were in a glass display case at Hutzler's Department Store. I held tightly to my book, *My Little Heart Prays*. The Virgin Mother on the cover had been looking kindly at me since I made my First Communion. Nowhere in its pages could I find a prayer for losing a father.

The incense hung in a thick cloud in front of the acolyte. This smell and the aroma of gladiolas on the altar nauseated me. The Eucharist formed a paste in my throat. When Father Smith read the eulogy, he spoke familiarly about my dad. He did not know Daddy.

Near the end of the service he intoned, "Before man are life and death, good and evil, whichever he chooses shall be given him." Had my father chosen?

What exactly caused Dad to die? Did the doctors do something wrong? Should they have known he was so sick? Would the lung tumor have killed him anyway? How bad was his heart? Did they do anything for the terrible pain in his leg? Was Daddy scared? Was he angry? What had happened?

I would spend the next four decades of my life searching for answers.

I have never solved the mystery of my father's foreshadowing or why he chose to share that knowledge with me.

Pop

I never made my peace with gladiolas, but I like other flowers, especially geraniums in the spring. I plant several dozen every year in the semicircle in my front yard. Their sublime blooms burst with a joy that continues into autumn.

The fat red flowers and green ivy leaves thrive even when neglected. They are an easy-going bunch not too demanding of water or fertilizer, just some plucking of the dried buds so new ones can replace the old. The aroma is unlike other floral scents, more earthy, reminiscent of the ground from whence they came.

My first job, at age 13, was as a floral assistant at a roadside stand. A fancy title to describe taking homegrown flowers from rusting coffee cans filled with murky water and wrapping the stems in newspaper. On the weekends, I helped an 80-year-old farmer, Pop, sell his bouquets to families visiting their deceased loved ones. We occupied a corner at Frankford and Belair Roads, ideally situated between church and cemetery making Saturday afternoons and Sunday mornings busy affairs. We had flowers for all seasons. Bursts of orange mums or pastel snapdragons peeked out of a long row of cans atop a low stone wall.

It wasn't only mourners who shopped at our stand. Potted red geraniums that wintered over in a shed went home with gardeners in the early spring. Pole beans, peppers, and red tomatoes made it a summer market.

At the end of the weekend, Pop let me have the left-over tomatoes, juice spilling out of my mouth as I bit the tough skin and slurped the insides. No tomato ever tasted as good.

We were open from Palm Sunday to Labor Day. If the weather held out, we showed up once a month at Columbus Day, Veteran's Day, Christmas, and New Year's with wreath decorations that Pop made by hand from dried leaves, branches, greenery, and pinecones.

"That will be 50 cents," I said in a practiced grown-up voice. I took the bunch of yellow daffodils and placed them carefully on a page from the Baltimore Sun (but not the comic section, which I adored), making sure to fold the bottom in before wrapping them completely.

The customer, a middle-aged man in a pressed blue suit, handed me a dollar. I produced two quarters for change from a cigar box resting on the cement ledge. He smiled and thanked me. Pop grinned, showing his few remaining yellow-brown teeth.

"Good job, girlie," Pop said. He gave me a dollar and a dime, my share for that day's sales. With my wages in hand, I felt the flush of responsible adulthood.

I had been introduced to Pop by my friend, Eileen—a girl my age who lived up the hill in a red brick rowhouse identical to mine. She occasionally worked at the flower stand and Pop had told her he needed more help. She knew my family could use the money.

My father had died three months earlier. My mother changed jobs.

She had been a keypunch operator downtown. I loved to hold the mysterious beige cards with holes denoting commands for a computer. Even better were the long sheets with punched out messages like "Congratulations, Esther" or "Happy Birthday, Mary." We strung them across the living room and marveled at their sophistication.

My mom switched to cleaning homes during the week and doctors' offices on weekends. My dad's death made keeping our home and raising me a financial hardship. Mom made more money as a maid, cash in hand. I tried to do my part at the flower stand.

As a city dweller with barely any grass sandwiched between other postage stamp yards, I knew nothing about plants. Pop taught me the colors and seasons of a garden as we sat on the stone wall, a torn beach umbrella erected over us as protection from the midday sun.

"You have to nip the suckers that grow between the stems, or the tomatoes won't grow big," he said, chewing some tobacco and spitting the brown residue into a nearby canister just recently emptied of its bouquet.

"Oh," I said, wondering what a sucker was and what the tomato plant looked like, what any of the flowers looked like, in their natural habitat.

One day, Pop needed help cutting flowers and transporting them to the stand. I eagerly agreed. Mom drove me to Pop's farm early on a Saturday morning.

The property was a mix of decay and vitality. The house, a worn wooden structure, had a sagging porch and screen door that didn't close. I imagined it as newly built—straight lines and fresh paint.

A picket fence shedding its coat surrounded the vegetable plants and flowers—a hodge-podge of red, yellow, and pink blooms. Stakes supported the heavy, ripening tomatoes that drooped to the ground. The pole beans climbed trellises with large pods waiting to be plucked. Near the gate stood aged implements—a hoe, rake, and shovel—slightly rusted, handles cracked, and dirt clumped on their working ends.

A scarecrow rested atop a wooden stake in the middle of the ½-acre plot. An Orioles baseball cap circa 1958 graced its head; the body dressed in an old shirt with large tears down the front. It was not the romantic version from the Wizard of Oz but instead resembled a figure that had met with a zombie attack. It suited the farm.

Pop wasn't a handsome man, with central balding and wisps of white fluff at the sides of his head. Brown aging spots dotted his face and arms, while fingers showed gnarled knuckles and perennially dirty nails. His clothing carried the stains of hours working in the soil; one strap of his overalls missing. I adored him.

He had a real family, grown-up kids with their own children, but on the weekends, he and I were family in that geranium-scented corner of the world.

Once I asked if I could call him Grandpa and he agreed, but it never stuck. He remained Pop.

I worked for him for three years on most Saturdays and Sundays. When business was slow, I would read a Daphne Du Maurier or Agatha Christie novel. Pop sat, resting his feet on an overturned milk crate. Sometimes we watched the heat shimmer on the black asphalt and the insects crawl along the sidewalk. Hot summer days in the city required languid actions. He spoke of his youth, the loss of his wife years earlier, the farm. I talked of school, my friends, and how I wanted to be a doctor.

At 16, I got a real job as a switchboard operator for an answering service. The pay was more than I could make on a busy weekend wrapping flowers. I walked to work, a block away from school, and took the bus home at the end of my five-hour shift.

Handling the telephone lines demanded that I gauge the importance of each call. It required clear speech and handwriting and knowing when to interrupt someone's dinner. I learned telephone shorthand like LWTC, left word to call, that I still use. The company had doctors, plumbers, and construction businesses as clients. I answered the phones with pride.

I stayed in touch with Pop through letters and cards on our birthdays and Christmas. We aged; the city changed. People visited cemeteries less frequently. The plastic and silk varieties of remembrance replaced the natural ones. The flower stand withered.

Eventually Pop sold the farm. Thinking back on it, I don't know how he held on as long as he did. The work was tough on the knees and back and especially on his arthritic hands. I couldn't do that work in my sixties. He had kept on until nearly 90.

I held on to my dream to become a doctor. When I graduated high school and college, I kept Pop apprised. He expressed pride in me and made me a pair of earrings from dime coins dated 1942 with the silver removed to outline the head of Mercury—an appropriate gift since that is the god of commerce and I learned business at Pop's knee.

We shared rare outings even when Pop's mobility failed him, and as I pursued my MD degree. A fellow student helped me load Pop into the front passenger seat of my Volkswagen Rabbit for a trip to the Inner Harbor. I pushed him in his wheelchair up and down along the dock. The breeze blew his few remaining head hairs as he breathed in the smell of the Chesapeake accompanied by whatever spice McCormick was processing that day.

"That's my girlie," Pop said. He reached up to pat my hand. "How about some ice cream?"

He knew I wouldn't refuse him a taste of this forbidden food or any other. As a budding doctor I knew his restrictions, but I rationalized that days of recreation were special, and he was getting older.

Towards the end of his life, he was admitted to the hospital where I was doing a clinical rotation as a third-year medical student. He had come in dehydrated with a urinary tract infection. He didn't recognize me when I entered his room.

"Quick, come here," Pop said. He urgently made rowing motions with his arms. He paused to extend a hand to me.

I took it and sat on the edge of the bed next to him.

"No, get up," he said, "in the boat." He patted the bed. I pulled my feet onto the mattress. He picked up the oars again and frantically guided the vessel.

"We'll be okay," I said.

Maybe we were at war, the Great War, and he was the ship's commander. In my blue scrubs, maybe he thought I was in a naval uniform. I huddled next to him, balancing on the bed. He seemed so small amid the sea of blankets and sheets. His arms thinned of muscle were bruised, common with the thin skin of the elderly. He continued to right the boat in the rough waves and then grabbed my hand to hold me steady.

My tears landed on his arm. Suddenly his energy left. He took in the hospital surroundings.

"Mary," he said, surprisingly alert.

"Yes, Pop," I said, leaning in to kiss his cheek, sunken, pale, and stubbled.

"I'm glad you came," he wheezed. "I'm really glad you came, girlie."

"Me, too," I whispered in his ear as I put my arms around him. We held on to each other for a while.

The rescue mission had tired him. I guided him down to the pillow. He closed his eyes, instantly asleep. I went back to caring for other patients, the boat not leaving my mind that day.

He died a few months later.

The Morgue

I rang the bell at the institutional metal door. The city sidewalk teemed with office workers starting a nine-to-five day. Automobiles honked and buses clanged over the trolley tracks.

"Can I help you?" a voice said from the intercom.

"I'm here from Seton High," I answered. The buzzer unlocked the door.

The bleak, gray foyer matched the concrete stone of the outside foundation. A plaque on the wall read, "Let conversation cease. Let laughter flee. *Hic locus est ubi mors gaudet succurrere vitae.* This is the place where death delights to help the living."

"Sign in here," the receptionist said, pushing a composition book towards me.

My signature was graceful—Catholic school calligraphy. In the column marked "Reason for visit," I wrote, "Government Day."

The office worker looked dubiously at this, picked up the phone, and dialed.

"Dr. Smith, I have a high school student here who says she's supposed to visit the Medical Examiner's Office today." A pause, then, "Yes sir. Will do."

"He says you are to come right in." She smiled. "No one has chosen our office in 15 years, since we started listing with the program."

Fifteen years—that was my age.

Choosing the morgue had seemed inspired when our sophomore class received a list of agencies willing to have kids shadow for the day. My friends picked city hall and the mayor's office, with visions of becoming sophisticated Girl-Fridays or uniformed court clerks. My dream was to be a physician. I reasoned I could learn about the human body by seeing it in the flesh.

Standing in the foyer, I felt dizzy.

The secretary pushed a button and the inner door clicked open. She waved me through. The corridor, dimly lit and dank, smelled of rotten food with an overlay of bleach. The hallway seemed to narrow and grow darker.

An older man called to me from a doorway farther down the hall, "This way, Miss."

I walked toward the human contact.

"Go, change in there, and leave your stuff in a locker," he said, pointing to a door labeled Women.

"Thank you," I said, heading into the room, grateful to leave the creepy hall behind.

On one wall, shelving contained folded surgical scrubs, the kind Dr. Kildare wore on television. The professional attire calmed me as I changed from my blue plaid school uniform. Pushing open the door on the opposite wall revealed the autopsy suite.

A pungent aroma assailed my nose, reminding me of unwrapping fresh beef to make a roast on Sundays, only much stronger. The lights were brighter than the hallway, making the air warm and stale. They reflected off the stainless-steel surfaces. Water ran continuously, splashing in the sinks at the tables' ends. Spilled blood and urine swirled into the drains.

Four dead people were lined up on the gurneys. The only kind of dead people I had ever seen were in their Sunday-best nestled in mahogany coffins. These folks lay on the cold metal, naked without even hospital gowns or bandaging.

Between the feet of each cadaver sat a bucket, containing discarded tissue already examined by the pathologists. A garbage can in the center of the room collected the innards when the buckets became full. One attendant made notes on a clipboard. Another stood near the door smoking a cigarette. Both wore bloody gloves.

Saws grinded, cutting through bone—skulls and ribs—to expose the internal viscera. Hanging scales swayed as dissected organs were placed inside. Instruments sat on cafeteria trays balanced across the thighs of the bodies.

Directly in front of me lay a corpse, chest caved in, scalp pulled forward covering his face to expose the skull. Blood pooled on the table, leaking from recently severed insides. A tall, thin doctor in a butcher's apron stood to the side. Yellow rubber gloves covered his hands extending to his elbows.

"Hello, I'm Dr. Smith. I would shake your hand, but…," he shrugged.

"Hi," I said. "Nice to meet you." My voice squeaked an octave higher than usual.

"Stand here," the doctor said, motioning me closer to the table. He handed me a matching pair of Rubbermaids. He retrieved an object, the size of a grapefruit, from a silver salad bowl. The thing was reddish brown with splotches of yellow. White rubbery tubes stuck out on one side.

"This is the heart," he said, dabbing it with a paper towel. He used a probe to point to a large rip in the muscle. Placing the organ on a cork board, he cut into a straw-like portion with a scalpel.

He said words beyond my understanding like coronary artery occlusion, myocardial infarction, and hypercholesterolemia, words that would become familiar to me much later in medical school. At the time, they brought scientific refinement to the macabre scene.

"Blood couldn't feed oxygen to the muscle because of the blocked vessel, leading to a heart attack," he explained. "Here."

He held the organ out to me.

Putting my hands together, palms up, like a communicant, I received this gift. The heart felt hard, except for the tear, which was soft like overripe fruit. The main artery, no bigger than a coffee stirrer, was closed off by a tiny glob of fat. Dr. Smith talked on, the words inaudible. My attention focused on the patient's anatomy. The stench and disgusting appearance of the morgue faded.

A human heart rested in my hands. Hours earlier, it beat inside someone's chest and then stopped. Like my father's had.

Did this man know he was going to die? Was it painful? Was he alone? Could a doctor have saved him? Did he have a family?

"Thank you," I managed, gently returning the organ to the pan.

Strength gathered in the rapid beating of my own heart. I watched as the pathologist continued with the man's autopsy.

Counting Fish

"So, you're Jumbelic," Dr. Zankel said, when I sat down in his office for the job interview. He puffed on his pipe, wild Einsteinian hair framing his face.

"Yes sir," I said as he flipped through my resume and transcript. I tugged at the hem of my skirt, smoothing it over my knees as if in the presence of Mother Superior though I had been out of Catholic high school for nearly two years.

"I see you had some trouble in Chemistry." He paused, inhaling the tobacco, little curls of smoke escaping as he exhaled.

My pre-planned explanation dried on my tongue.

"You have really turned things around in Biology," he said. He nodded, examining my grades.

"Yes, I really have, sir." I had repeated my problematic course and taken classes throughout the summer and mini-mester sessions.

He looked at me, leaned forward, and tapped his pipe into an ashtray on his desk.

I held my breath.

It had been three months since I'd seen the job advertised on the bulletin board at my university: "Seeking an upper-level biology major with a 3.75 GPA for part-time work."

The only problems were that I was a sophomore, and my grades were well below the magna cum laude requirement. I applied anyway.

The research assistant position at Martin Marietta sounded perfect for me: the company was located nearby the UMBC campus and paid well, much better than my minimum-wage job making subs at Niko's. My scholarship didn't fund all my tuition and I lived at home rather than in the dorms to save the cost of housing. I needed the money.

They had hired someone else. I remained undeterred, calling the company once a week just in case a new opportunity turned up. The months went by. I received a call from Dr. Zankel, a head physicist for Martin Marietta's Research and Development division. He had a summer opening.

I sat before him awaiting the verdict.

"When this job came up, yours was the first name I thought of." He pointed to a dozen pink memos on the desk—all with my name on them. "Something about your persistence made me think you'd be perfect."

I grinned. I got the job.

At first it was a summer position, which extended into part-time after-school work, evolving to full-time employment as I finished a few credits in my senior year before starting medical school. I became a research assistant, brought home a regular paycheck, paid tuition, and even had money to give my mother for rent while living at my childhood home. It was as perfect as I'd imagined when I first saw the job notice.

Dr. Zankel and I worked together for three years.

My first project at Martin Marietta was documenting fish populations in the heat effluent of a local nuclear power plant.

I grew up in the city of Baltimore at the mouth of the Chesapeake Bay —an urban girl, familiar with bricks and asphalt not the sea. I had been in rowboats and canoes along the Severn River, paddled by high school paramours. Until this job, the most exciting water experience had been the steep drop and volcanic spray of the Log Flume ride at Hershey Park.

I found myself on a trawler in the middle of the night. Dr. Zankel had organized a field expedition for data collection using a sonar transducer and trawling net. There were three of us on this vessel: my boss, a co-worker, and me. Dr. Z was captaining the boat.

The wind and rain lashed us. We tried to stay upright as the boat swayed. A loud rhythmic banging emitted from below.

"Mary, go down in the hold and secure the instruments," Dr. Z said.

The other worker, a more senior student, had already attempted this but was vomiting over the side of the boat.

"Ok, no problem," I said.

I felt eager to help. Up to this expedition, I had sat at a desk, studying charts and graphs, and calculating total numbers of different-sized fish. This open-water adventure excited me as we actively collected sonic and physical data.

The edges and hood of my rain slicker flapped. Even layered in tee shirt, sweatshirt, and jacket, I felt chilly. As I stepped down into the hold, the warmth wrapped around me. I held onto the rail and widened my stance for balance, the boat rocking back and forth and up and down. One of the stabilizing ropes had come loose, its clip clacking as it swung against the cabinet. I reattached the line and checked the other connections. The green lights affirmed that all systems were operating.

I ascended the ladder and climbed back onto the deck.

"Sit here." Dr. Z patted the seat next to him. "Keep an eye on the horizon. We'll be through these swells in a few minutes."

The other student laid at the stern, bundled in an orange life vest and army surplus blanket. He looked like a drowned flower. Dr. Z followed my gaze.

"He'll perk up when we get back to shore. You and I can collect the data. How would you like to steer?"

I settled onto the soft cushion as the boat tossed through the waves.

A pipe nestled in my boss's mouth though he wasn't smoking. This functioned as his talisman. He said he thought more clearly with it. His gray hair danced above his head. His thick, black-framed glasses, and dark turtleneck made him look like a scientific version of the captain from Tintin. He was just missing the hat.

I took the wheel.

Presaging Peter

Was this Peter? I never expected to see anyone I knew.

I stood in the damp morgue that could have served as a set for a horror film. Not much had changed from 11 years earlier. Just three months shy of graduating from the University of Maryland School of Medicine, I had returned for an elective in forensic pathology.

My four-week rotation had started that morning.

I saw a man on one of the gurneys, eerily familiar. Black, straight hair stuck out on the right side of his head as if he had just run his hand through it. Bare feet seemed too large for his short frame. His face in profile was turned slightly away from me. The hair, the brown skin tone, and the build reminded me of an old friend.

The other patients in the room ranged in age from 15 to 60 years old. This man appeared in his mid-twenties. Peter would be my age, 26. We hadn't seen each other since high school, a lifetime ago. My passage had taken me from Catholic girls' school to university to study medicine. He had transitioned from Baltimore Polytechnic Institute to what exactly? I didn't know.

The attending doctor read each chart moving from one exam table to the next. He summarized the findings for the group as we students and residents trailed after him like ducklings.

Our team approached Peter's look alike. Blood rushed to my face and pulsed in my ears. This man was handsome like my friend, but the effervescence gone, his perennial smile absent. Hands peeked out from beneath the sheets; the records too far away for me to read.

Only shuffling feet and scritching pens could be heard in the lulls between the doctor's words. Laughter and conversation had ceased.

When did I meet Peter? Sophomore year? At a local mixer when my high school beau, Michael, introduced us? Maybe Peter tagged along with Michael for our daily rendezvous at Wyman Park or we ran into each other at the Baltimore City festival? Or was it on the long commute to school?

Bus number 22 carried students from an intersection of neighborhoods to schools miles away from our homes. As it traveled down Erdman Avenue, laughter and gossip fanned out along provisional antennules of teenage desire. The atmosphere tingled. For most of us, ensconced in religious or gender-specific schools, the travel provided excitement and diversity.

Those bus rides defined my high school days. I stood on the corner waiting for the 7:20 a.m. connection. The early hour and second ride of the morning might have made it a slog. Yet the hiss of the bus braking as it pulled to the curb imbued me with anticipation. The door thumped open, and I stepped up, handing the transfer slip and my ID to the driver. Glancing at the passengers with 15-year-old feigned nonchalance, I surfed my way to the back as the vehicle jerked forward.

One day, Peter grabbed my notebook and lifted it up to show everyone, my attention held hostage as he grinned. Neat writing in ballpoint filled the pages. "Michael and Mary Forever" scripted in blue on the inside cover. Red hearts decorated the words.

I lunged for the book, half falling on him in my effort. Michael, a full head taller than Peter, recaptured it. He read the words and laughed, punching Peter's shoulder as he returned it to me. I exited the bus at my stop.

On the pavement, I transferred my school pack to my left arm. With my right, I unrolled my waistband to lengthen the uniform skirt to knee level. Glancing back, I saw the two teenage boys, faces pressed to the window, kissing the glass. I stuck out my tongue.

My heart ached for the three of us and that long ago morning.

When rounds finished, everyone headed to their posts; busy doctors confident in their assignments. During my reverie, we walked past the man who might be Peter. I hesitated—turn back or keep going?

The chart sat at his feet, containing his name, presumptive diagnosis, and medical history. Perspiration beaded my forehead, the room unbearably hot. I blinked rapidly as if to change the frame of the picture like a View Master toy.

Not him. Not him. Not him. The *lub dub* of my heart followed the rhythm of the words.

I bent over to read the case number written in black permanent marker on a little cardboard tag attached by wire to his right big toe. I looked carefully now at Peter's corpse.

He lay face-up on the gurney, dressed in a ratty tee-shirt and frayed jeans. Gone was the ironed white shirt and neat blue pants he sported in high school. A sisal rope wound tightly around his neck. The ligature bit in, chafing and grooving the skin. Thirteen knots formed the classic hangman's noose. His tongue stuck out, dried at the tip, and caught between teeth, a distorted gesture from a fright-night mannequin. Saliva dotted his cheek and chin as his head tilted to the side. A stale aroma of cigarettes and weed suspended in the air.

I looked at the records—"Body found hanging from fire escape, back of apartment, 7 a.m. by city workers. No suicide note. No evidence of trauma. Police, EMS at scene." Succinct and methodical phrases, like his death, and cold like his body. A life summed up in 25 words.

Metal banged against metal as assistants set up workstations for the autopsies. A saw buzzed as one of the technicians began opening a chest. The smell of internal organs reached my nose, reminding me of a butcher shop in Lexington Market, less than six blocks away. Overhead fluorescent lights quivered. Dizziness and nausea threatened.

Maybe I was wrong. How easy it would be to conflate names and appearances. I didn't trust my memory. This man only resembled my friend and might be another person with the same name and look. Was Peter's family name a common East Indian name? I did not want to accept that this body belonged to my friend.

I hurried from the morgue, running up the stairs to the third-floor library propelled by images of gallows and tight knots. It was a place of sanctuary separated from the grim scene below. It also had a telephone. I picked up the receiver and dialed.

Brrring. Brrring. Brrring.

I listened to the sound of the phone ringing, waiting for my friend to pick up.

"Hello," Michael said, infusing me with comfort and sadness. I began to cry. It had been months since we had spoken. "Mary? What's wrong? Baby, you can tell me."

The story came out in a cascade of words describing Peter and his body, punctuated by my crying.

He took it in and parroted my concerns.

"Are you sure?" he asked. "I mean, really sure. You got to be sure."

I inhaled slow, deep breaths.

"The name and age are right, and it looks just like him," I said. Tears had gathered in my mouth. I coughed to clear my throat. "They're supposed to check these things. Forensic ID and all that."

"I'm going to make a few calls. Get back to me in 15," he said and hung up.

I sat down in the worn leather chair.

Forensic classics—*Disposition of Toxic Drugs and Chemicals in Man* and *Gunshot Wounds: Practical Aspects of Firearms, Ballistics, and Forensic Techniques*—stared at me from the surrounding tall bookshelves. The Bible of forensic pathology *(Medicolegal Investigation of Death)*, co-authored by Russell Fisher, the Chief Medical Examiner here in Maryland, was laid open on the long table. Phrases levitated from the open pages: human body, asphyxia, postmortem.

The detailing of lethal violence, the gruesome sleuthing overwhelmed me. What did the differing calibers of guns mean to the mother who lost her son? Or the knife wounding pattern to a grieving partner?

I stared at the clock, a replica from my high school classroom, as if waiting for the 3:40 dismissal bell. Just like then, the minute hand seemed to travel in reverse.

Michael picked up on the first ring.

"I spoke to his sister," he said. "The family was called early this morning. They already identified him."

I sunk into myself. The Hindu mother, father, sister saw all of it—the noose, his face, the rawness of dying. Would they have an open casket before the cremation? What were their thoughts on his Karma? Did suicide violate Dharma?

I did not know what happened after death but refused to believe Peter would be suspended between heaven and hell as I was taught by the Catholic Church.

"I haven't talked to him in quite a while." Michael spoke slowly. "He drifted away, got into drugs. I haven't seen him since he left the Air Force. He was discharged, only did a year."

They had enlisted together, going to serve their country as the war in Vietnam ended, hoping to get a paid college education from the military.

"I didn't know how bad it was. I thought it was just a wild phase. With the drugs, you know. I should have done more...," Michael's voice trailed off.

I felt the same helplessness, remorse, and regret. Yet I hadn't seen Peter in nearly nine years. I wasn't friends with this adult; I only knew the teen. Grief swirled around me like morning fog over the Bay Bridge.

I hung up the phone and closed my eyes, which brought snapshots of a man swinging at the end of a rope alternating with my friends mugging for the camera. Peter's shoeless feet must have been cold touching the metal of the fire escape. An urge to run away seized me, to flee from the rot and despair seeping up from the basement.

I called downstairs and told the chief resident that I felt ill. He assumed I was squeamish and couldn't handle the dissections in the morgue. I didn't correct him.

I met Michael that evening in Fell's Point. We had remained friends since high school though we hadn't seen each other in over a year. Sitting at a booth, a pitcher of Natty Boh on the table, we reminisced about us, the couple we were for four years. We told meandering stories of duckpin bowling, ice skating at Memorial Stadium, Egg Foo Young at Jimmy Woo's, the film *Friends* at the Charles Theater.

Unhappy memories punctured the recollections.

Michael and I, black and white, had had to tread carefully in our urban landscape. In the early 1970s, people tossed trash and disparaging remarks at us from cars as we walked hand in hand down the street. Aluminum cans and paper cups hit us with the same vehemence as the words accompanying them. Sticky soda coated our arms and fueled us with fear and anger.

It had only been five years before Michael and I met, that the Supreme Court issued a ruling in *Loving v. Virginia*, one state away, legalizing interracial marriage. We didn't make it that far.

We turned to the sweeter memories.

Throughout the evening we chorused "Remember that time?" We cried and then uncontrollably giggled.

"Want some oyster shooters?" Michael said.

"Absolutely," I said. "This month has an R in it, right?" I referred to the local theory that oysters could only be eaten from September to April.

Old Bay and lemon coated the lump of seafood in my shot glass. Vodka layered the top. As I tossed it in my mouth, the delicious mixture tweaked my salivary glands and the spice rose in my nose.

We finally spoke of our friend. I saw the three of us, united colors of Benetton, impossibly young, hopeful, immortal. The dead Peter blurred at the edges, then receded. His body rested in the pull-out drawer at the morgue. Only memories of the living Peter remained. Our words made his image tangible. We recreated his laugh and his smile.

We stayed through last call.

The next morning, I returned to the Medical Examiner's Office. Until the alarm rang at six, I hadn't been convinced I wanted to step foot in there again. Rounds were about to start. I checked the roster. Peter had been picked up by the funeral home the prior evening.

Even if the corpse had been there, my friend was not. The clang of gurneys, the conversation of staff, and the drip of a faucet replaced the absence of Peter's laughter.

Scents and Sensibilities

Herbal Essence?

Inhaling deeply, I envisioned the shampoo bottle and logo—a long-haired goddess, tresses decorated with flowers. Did this icon survive the seventies?

I parted the woman's hair carefully with my gloved hands like a stylist about to apply color. My work paused. The odor created intimacy. Ten years into my career as a Medical Examiner and the scent of botanicals blossomed from my youth.

"Are you okay, Dr. J?" my assistant said.

Was I? The aroma lingered, as on a bath towel in my remote Baltimore home.

"Smell that?" I said.

The technician leaned in and sniffed. "Shampoo?"

"Yes. She recently washed her hair. It's still damp."

"Is that important?" His eyes took in the rest of her injured body.

"Every detail matters in a homicide." Then I added, "In any case really."

I had an impulse to explain this truth; to elaborate on the science. Instead, we stood respecting the quiet in the morgue amidst this fragrant echo.

A decade earlier, in 1987, my mentor, the Deputy Chief at the Cook County Medical Examiner's Office, told me to use as many senses as possible during an autopsy. Dr. Kirschner was Jewish but looked Amish with a well-trimmed salt and pepper beard and no mustache. His face along with his balding scalp reminded me of the action figure Dr. Hugo Strange, a nemesis of Batman, except Dr. K maintained a rim of hair around the sides of his head.

He may have looked like a supervillain, but he was my forensic sensei. I had met him while still in my pathology residency, spending every available elective credit to be at the Chicago Morgue.

"What do you mean, use all of my senses?" I asked.

Doctors readily used acuity. He emphasized more than visualization. Rounds had finished. Fifteen bodies waited for us.

"Of course, everyone uses their eyes, but you also need to touch," Dr. K said. "Feel the organs to determine if they are normal or diseased. Use your fingertips to find abnormalities. Is it soft, hard? Does it break apart easily or is it tough?"

My pathology training at the hospital over the prior three years had emphasized these tactile descriptions of specimens. I inspected tumors removed during surgery—detailing texture, assessing solidity. This was already a part of my regimen. The rest of his advice proved more novel.

"Hearing is important, too. Catching the sound of air or gas escaping from the body," he said, then raising an eyebrow, "and listening for insect activity."

I winced. The life cycle of the blowfly became known to me in my forensic fellowship. I didn't like flies in any of their life stages, but I especially hated their infant forms.

"You can tell how many maggots are in a decomposing body by the volume of the sound when they're eating." Dr. K explained tallying numbers on the maggot census.

I abhorred the crunching noise they made.

He tapped the side of his nose with an index finger. "But this right here is the most important tool of all. Use it all the time. Don't conceal its power like the cops do with Vicks VapoRub. It will tell you where someone has been, their habits, when something is different than expected, even why they died."

Smells filled the autopsy suite: blood, body fluids, rot, decay. A kaleidoscope of aromas that seemed to require endurance not analysis; odors to be avoided and overpowered with orange-scented deodorizer or absorbed with coffee grounds.

Yet he instructed me to go beyond the unpleasantness and unmask what lay beneath.

His words proved salient.

After I finished an autopsy on a middle-aged man found dead on his front porch, my head pounded, and I felt nauseous. Only Carl, my technician, and I were in the Chicago morgue.

"You feel okay, Carl?" I said.

"Yeah. You?" Carl said.

"Not really. Smell anything?"

"No."

"The stomach contents smell weird. I'm going to talk to the lab. Why don't you just cover him up and take a break."

"Okay, Dr. J," Carl said.

I headed to the chief toxicologist's office.

"Knock, knock," I said at the open door. "Mike, I have a question."

He smiled broadly, always eager to share chemical and pharmacologic information.

I told him about the case, that I was feeling sick, and the weird smell of the gastric contents.

"What did it smell like? Bitter almonds?"

"Well, yes."

"Wait here."

He unlocked a secure cabinet and retrieved a small brown bottle. He opened the cap and directed me to smell it.

"Yeah, that's it." I marveled.

Only 50% of people have the ability to detect the aroma of the deadly poison cyanide. I did but hadn't recognized it.

"We usually test everyone when they start working here. Sorry we were late getting to you."

He went on to explain that the first few cases of poisoning in the Tylenol tampering in 1982 had slipped past the noses of the pathologist and technician. Seven people had died. After this, the office ensured that at least one member of any team working on an autopsy had the ability to smell cyanide.

Carl could not smell cyanide and he hadn't been close to the stomach contents, where the poison mixed with gastric acid to produce the deadly vapors that made me sick. I called downstairs to tell Carl.

Fresh air and time were the tonic I needed; I felt better by dinner.

This nasal ability developed into the early warning system that aided me in six future cases, alerting me long before the sickening effects of the poison.

My olfactory sense found purpose in noticing what a person had eaten, or their state of cleanliness. The more I used it, the more astute it became. I passed this skill to trainees.

Medical students came to my office in Syracuse from Upstate Medical University where I taught them the principles of dissection through performing autopsies. They were naive to nasal potential, like I had been in the distant past.

I held up a container of gastric contents for them to sniff. They looked away. They coughed and stepped back from the gurney.

"Go ahead, smell it," I said, demonstrating how to waft a hand over the open jar to bring the air particles towards the face. A brave upperclassman waved his hand over the container.

"Beer," he said, eyes widening. "I thought it would be like puke."

My nose became my sentry. It gathered information, and calculated behavior. Common scents infiltrated the malodorous background impressing me with their poignancy.

"Look at this," the technician said.

He pointed to the mouth of an older man. A pink tablet lodged in the teeth and coated the tongue. The wintergreen of Pepto-Bismol reached into my nostrils. The man had taken the medication to relieve indigestion. It did nothing for his heart attack.

The smell transported me to his pain, making visceral his final breath. He expected to feel relief from the stab of discomfort as he popped the tablet in his mouth but collapsed even before he could swallow.

On an average Saturday, I noted a corpse's external physical appearance. I described the color and size of tattoos, moles, and surgical scars. Lifting the man's arm, a familiar scent emanated from the pit. Hints of nutmeg and anise captured in dots of anti-perspirant stuck onto axillary hairs.

"What does that remind you of?" I asked my assistant.

Used to my quizzes, he took a whiff and said, "I know it. Um. Wait a minute. Old Spice?"

"Yes."

He nodded without any sense of accomplishment. The olfactory remnant of the corpse's life sobered us.

I pictured the young man applying the bar of deodorant: one swipe, two, preparing for his day. The pleasing bouquet evoked a time before the car crash, when the only care was unpleasant body odor or shirt stains. The smell lingered after the unexpected interaction with the semi, the exploding airbag, the shattered windows.

I needed air.

The fragrance of sentience entwined with the grave throughout my 25 years in pathology creating a juxtaposition of normalcy and the unforeseen.

Molecules of Chanel #5 rose from the skin of a woman who collapsed at a restaurant. My mother shared that same fragrance as she headed off to a Knights of Columbus dance. The acrid nail polish from a recent manicure floated above a teen overdose. The identical aroma greeted me when I shared a spa day with a friend. Traces of Obsession on a man collapsed at work blended with my husband's favorite cologne. Vapors of hair spray drifted in the air from a nursing home patient and re-emerged from another can as I fixed my hair before testifying in court.

Everyday smells imprinted in my quotidian catalog of death. The scents traversed the boundary between before and after; crossing the frontier that separates the world outside and inside the morgue. A permeable wall of memory surrounded me.

Bubblegum, popcorn, pizza, orange juice, vomitus, beer, hair gel, body spray, toothpaste, mouthwash, blood, shaving cream, lotions, cigarettes, marijuana, chocolate, coffee, urine, coconut, lemon, cinnamon, lavender, pus, lilac, rose, satsuma, eucalyptus, spearmint, feces, grape, cherry, watermelon, cumin, garlic.

Proustian moments.

Part II

Chicago

The flesh of the dead
becomes as palpable to me
as my own.

The Shoe

I imagined the seventh grader resting her left foot on her right knee, pressing the marker firmly to decorate the shoe. I used a magnifying glass to discern the pattern, dark letters scrawled on the midsole of a dirty white sneaker, edges bleeding a pinkish red—"DENISE." Indefinable scribbling followed the name, as unfathomable to me as the reason she lay on the morgue gurney.

I was 32 years old and four-months pregnant, expecting my first child. Ever since I announced the happy event, the photographer at the Cook County Medical Examiner's Office took monthly Polaroids of me in profile in my green scrubs. My baby bump hardly showed. He thumbtacked the photos to the corkboard in the morgue office. In them, I smiled broadly. That day, I didn't feel like smiling.

Denise, the girl on my table, was slight at five-feet tall and barely 100 pounds, though with the postmortem changes, it was hard to know what she weighed before; her 12-year-old body was unrecognizable in its decomposition. Six days in a boarded-up garage in Chicago in an August heat wave had not been kind to the small girl.

Her body was unnaturally discolored, except for a patch where her belly made contact with the concrete floor. Her clothing had the same red-black color as her skin—blending in a wet miasma.

The shriveled and disfigured skin of her face stretched tightly against the bone. A sneer exposed her upper teeth; dried lips curled up and away. The epidermis had loosened from the fingers and toes. Maggots found the warm cavities and burrowed into crevices in fabric.

The right shoe remained on the body but without its shoelace. The left shoe, the one I examined, had been near her head in the same condition. I found the laces. One was used to tie her hands behind her back. The other was tied around her neck, so tight it formed a taut 3-inch diameter circle.

From police investigators I had learned that Denise was visiting relatives in South Chicago from her home in a suburb 30-minutes away. She helped with babysitting. She had discovered choir and tennis. The whole summer had been hot. The temperature reached 100 degrees on the day she disappeared. She had gone outside, maybe for a breath of fresh air or maybe for adventure in the way innocents do.

Jerome and Denise met on the stoop of her cousin's home in the late afternoon of the day she was last seen alive. They shared a flirtatious repartee.

"She's only 12," Denise's cousin said. "Get off the porch and stay away." She pulled the girl inside the house. "She's 12," she said as she slammed the door.

Jerome lived in the neighborhood and was on parole, released a few months earlier after serving time for rape. Rumor had it the previous assault happened in the same garage, a one-minute walk from the cousin's house.

I held the shoe in my gloved hands. The eyelets gaped open; the tongue drooped inside. The tread was worn, and the sides scuffed. It looked naked without its laces; embarrassed to be found in this state of undress.

When did the unlacing happen?

It must have been before Jerome pulled the black tank top off since the shoelace was found underneath the shirt also tied around her neck. Was it before he unzipped, unbuttoned, and pulled her pants down? Or after he pressed her face-down onto the floor?

Who unlaced the shoes? Did the 24-year-old threaten Denise with a knife or gun while the girl shakily undid them? Did he grab the footwear from her and do it himself? Why was the right shoe still on her foot? Did he calmly place it back after she died?

Jerome never said how the shoelaces ended up around the girl's neck and wrists. He claimed consensual sex.

DNA testing was in its infancy then. Even with modern techniques, extreme decomposition can preclude scientific results. None of Jerome's bodily fluids were identified. No drop of saliva, blood, or semen from him was found. In 1988, my description of Denise's body and bondage provided the sole evidence of homicide. It was enough for a sentence of natural life imprisonment.

It takes me 36 seconds to unlace one of my sneakers. I've timed it. Maybe it can be done more quickly. I have rheumatoid arthritis and so my hands aren't as adept as they used to be. Still, that would be more than a minute to remove both laces.

A minute in a dark and dank garage, waiting.

Pizza Hut

"I don't know," my mother said.

She followed up on a question I had asked—did her parents have any diseases? I was pregnant with my first child.

"They didn't have any, or you don't know?" I said.

We sat at the Pizza Hut near Michigan Avenue in Chicago. Mom had moved from Baltimore to the city to help with the baby. That day we went out to lunch near my former residency training program at Northwestern Memorial Hospital.

I took a big bite of my slice, the cheese stretching out from the plate to my mouth. Nearing my third trimester, I was hungry all the time.

I knew the prevalence of heart problems on Dad's side; it had killed him at the age of 69 and his twin brother a decade earlier. Having met some of Dad's siblings and cousins, I observed their ills but thought of them as problems of the elderly.

Mom's side of the family remained a mystery. She was an only child. Her parents had died before I was born. I never met any of her relatives.

"What's with the third degree?" she said, sounding irritable.

"I just worry about the baby and medical issues."

She sipped her Diet Coke. I waited.

"I don't know, Mary."

This puzzled me. Did she mean her parents didn't share details of illness with her? Or were they healthy up until they died? Or maybe she didn't remember.

"Mom, please. It's important to me. I'm a doctor after all."

I knew she was proud always introducing me as her daughter, the doctor.

"Just leave it."

We sat in stubborn silence. She adopted this tactic whenever I asked too many questions. As a child I peppered her for information: Who was your first love? What was your mother like? How did you meet Daddy? I wanted her to create a vivid picture for me. My father had given me rich tales of his youth, an immigrant's son growing up in the coal-mining hills of Pennsylvania.

My mother gave clipped answers. She loved the boy next door, Raymond. He died at 13. Her mother liked to cook. She had roses in the backyard. Mom never cooked or gardened. I wanted more—whining, begging, and yelling. She kept to her brevity.

It took a lot of coaxing for her to tell me how she met my dad. I imagined a romantic dance or elegant dinner party. It turns out he was walking down the sidewalk past her house on North Avenue while she was washing the marble front stoop.

"It's super important for your grandson," I finally said.

She had longed for a grandchild since the day I married two years earlier. I knew she had wanted a dozen children of her own. I was her only, born in the 12th year of her marriage.

"I was adopted," she said in a voice someone might use with a waitress —'I'll take the fish.'

The room grew cold, my stomach nauseous.

When I was 10 years old, I believed that I had been adopted. No similarity between my mother and me was enough to convince me otherwise.

"You look just like your mom," a neighbor remarked.

"You're the spittin' image of Esther," one of her friends said.

I didn't see it.

I noted the divergence of personality: my insatiable need to read and learn contrasted with her lack of concern for history or science, my drive to solve a puzzle versus her Zen-like acceptance, my need to understand the past at odds with her life that seemed to exist without history. These differences felt urgent. I went on a quest.

Feigning a stomachache, I avoided the weekly family trip to Eddie's Supermarket. I stayed home and snuck into my parents' bedroom. Searching the top drawer of their dresser, I discovered an S&H green stamp book, a Metropolitan life insurance policy, a U.S. savings bond, an envelope penciled with a Colts' football play, and scrap paper tabulated with monthly bills. The absence of my birth certificate confirmed my fear.

When my parents returned home, they found me crying on the sofa. "You're not my mother," I said between sobs.

My mother calmly told me the details of giving birth to me—how I came out early at only eight-months gestation, after 36 hours of labor, weighing only four pounds. Daddy visited me every day as I lay in the incubator in the neonatal care unit.

I hugged her tightly.

"What are you saying?" I said. "When were you adopted? What happened to your parents? Why didn't you ever tell me, Mom?"

"I don't know," she said and in a gesture of generosity, added "I don't remember any of that. Charles and Irene were the only parents I ever knew. I think my real ones died in a car accident. Now, quit pestering me with questions. Just leave it."

For me, this was not nearly enough.

The truth of her upbringing had little impact on our day-to-day lives. I rationalized that she hadn't known much more about the adoption than she told me. It didn't matter to her. Joshua was born healthy at full term, with only 15 hours of labor. Mom helped raise him. I had no time to research the circumstances of her early life.

She didn't want to either.

BUCKETS

THE infant lay on the gurney wearing only a dry, disposable diaper, though the top of his head was still damp. He was a cherub—plump cheeks, wisps of hair, and fat little limbs with only the wings missing.

My assistant, Carl, and I stared at the body, cold and small, on the stainless-steel table. We had just finished morning rounds. This baby was 10 months old, learning to crawl and pull himself up. He had toppled headfirst into a five-gallon bucket, being used under an open sink to trap water from a leaky pipe. The pail had just enough murky liquid to cover his nose and mouth.

I shivered.

My son, Joshua, was six months old, learning to sit up and reach for things. His strong legs supported him when Daddy held him upright. He couldn't yet pull himself up to stand or be coordinated enough to crawl, but the ability to explore his environment was nearing. Most babies will do all of that by their first birthday.

"It's a shame," Carl said.

Babies evoked sorrow in the morgue with their tiny forms dwarfed by the magnitude of their surroundings. Carl looked at me, perhaps checking that I would be okay for this autopsy.

"I know," I said. "Let's get the x-rays."

Pediatric cases required extensive investigation, searching for signs of abuse or neglect. Even so, I finished the autopsy in less than an hour. The dissection was easy; the organs were perfectly healthy except for lots of fluid frothing out of the heavy lungs when I cut them open. I listed "Drowning" as the cause of death, and the manner, "Accident."

I left the morgue and headed toward the offices. I knocked on Dr. Kirschner's open door.

He looked up from his desk and smiled, distinctive creases forming on his inner cheeks. He waved me to a seat. Having been in academia for years before going into forensic pathology, he enjoyed supervising my research. In my fellowship, he acted as my main instructor; we had grown close.

"Good morning," he said as I settled in the office chair. Noticing my glum expression he added, "Rough one?"

"Yeah," I said. "I had another baby drowning."

He raised his eyebrows. "You want to look into this?"

"Yes. It was identical to the one I did a month ago. Head down in a five-gallon industrial bucket."

He nodded.

"How far back should I go with the records?" I said.

"Collect about five years of data." He leaned back in his chair. "You know babies can drown in any open water. Bathtubs, swimming pools, lakes. Even toilet bowls."

"I know but people already realize those dangers. Parents might not be aware of this hazard. I am shocked that these babies drowned. The buckets didn't even tip over. The moms found their little ones with legs and feet sticking straight up out of the pail."

"Go ahead. Look at all cases of drowning in children less than three years old."

I requested all the files from our medical records department. Twelve children, aged nine-to-16-months-old, had drowned in these industrial buckets. They accounted for a quarter of all drownings in children younger than three in Chicagoland. Most pails were being used for mopping.

Children at that age have larger heads, a high center of gravity, still-developing motor coordination, and innate curiosity. They reached in to touch the water and couldn't push themselves out. The strong, parallel sides, and sturdy construction of the five-gallon plastic containers made it hard for a top-heavy toddler to get out once the child had fallen in.

I tabulated data, wrote the report, and researched the references. I edited, rewrote, and re-edited the abstract, introduction, materials and methods, results, and comments. My conclusion stated, "Parents and health care officials must be warned of this drowning hazard and of the danger of using these five-gallon containers in the presence of toddlers."

I considered sending the case study for publication to one of the national forensic journals. Dr. K had other ideas.

"Submit the paper to *JAMA*," he said.

The Journal of the American Medical Association, in publication since 1883, is an international scientific magazine. All articles submitted are peer-reviewed by professionals working in the same field. About 5% of papers submitted are accepted for publication.

"There's no way," I said, feeling intimidated by the prestige of the journal.

"Look, if you publish in a forensic journal, pathologists will read it and say, 'Yeah, I've seen that.' If you publish it in *JAMA*, primary-care physicians will see it, and the news media might pick up on it. It will have a greater impact, warning more people of the dangers of these buckets."

Maybe a pediatrician or family practitioner would then caution parents of the fatal potential of a seemingly harmless household item. Maybe NPR would discuss it in a weekly medical news segment and alert listeners.

"It will never get published," I said.

"You have to shoot for the stars. This is too important to bury in a magazine for medical examiners."

His advice sounded sanguine despite my insecurity; I did as he instructed.

The day *JAMA* accepted the paper for publication, I ran to Dr. K's office.

"We did it," I said.

"You did it," he said.

The article got a lot of media attention and resulted in warning labels on the buckets. If you go into Home Depot or Lowe's, you can find these five-gallon containers emblazoned with an image of a toddler reaching into the bucket and a large red warning circle over the child, then the words "Children can fall into bucket and drown. Keep children away from bucket with even a small amount of liquid."

Everything I know about being a forensic pathologist, I learned from Dr. K. He showed me how to evaluate a case of child abuse or a death in custody by the police. His specialty had been ferreting out human-rights abuses. He traveled to the Balkans, Africa, and South America to uncover victims of political massacre or desaparecidos. He instilled in me the need to examine death on a larger scale, beyond the singular loss, but never to lose sight of that one person on the gurney.

"Whoever saves a single life is considered by scripture to have saved the whole world." This quote from the Talmud, a Jewish holy book, exemplified Dr. Kirschner's attitude. He taught me to accept the mantle of responsibility of learning from the dead to help the living.

First Interview

I felt queasy in the small, overheated room. Dry, too, as if my skin was baked phyllo dough. My heart beat loudly in my ears, a sure sign of elevated blood pressure. My chest throbbed.

I was still breastfeeding my one-year-old, Joshua, only once in the evening at bedtime, but it was past the usual hour. Sipping a black coffee to moisten my mouth, I wondered if the caffeine would keep me and the baby awake later. As if what I was going through wasn't enough by itself to create insomnia.

"Would you like some water, Doc?" a police officer asked me. Maybe he noticed the grimace on my face as I tasted the precinct brew.

"No, thanks. I'm fine," I said. The corners of my mouth cracked slightly with the effort to smile. The coffee swirling in my empty stomach, my physical discomfort, the unfamiliar setting, and the evening hour gathered in a surreal mix.

In an interrogation room at the Central Station of the Chicago Police Department, I sat face to face with a mother accused of murdering all six of her children. In addition to the killer and me, there were two men from the homicide division—the lead detective with whom I had worked closely, and his partner, the one who offered me water. I was an Assistant Medical Examiner at the Cook County office, my first job out of forensic pathology training.

Just an hour earlier my family had been headed home from the airport when my pager sounded. I became annoyed as I pulled the black plastic case from my travel bag. Technically, I was still on vacation. The noise woke my son in the back seat.

"Oh, look what you did now," my mother said, sitting next to the toddler seat and trying to return the binky to my little boy's mouth. Joshua accepted it as my mom cooed and shushed him.

"What is it, honey?" my husband said as he drove. The April temperature had dipped below freezing. The wind gusted and occasional snowflakes fell due to the air currents over Lake Michigan. The cold and darkness swallowed our car as we headed into the city.

"It's the downtown police station," I said.

"But you're not on call."

He was right. I wasn't on duty until the next day. This 8 p.m. Sunday page reached me returning from a visit with my in-laws in Florida. Just that morning we had walked the beach. I still felt stray sand between my toes inside my sneakers.

My line of work didn't respect personal boundaries. Though we didn't know it at the time, this was just one of many interruptions because of my job—some in the middle of the night, some lasting weeks at a time—upending plans and schedules. My family never got used to it, but they accepted it.

I opened the glove compartment and retrieved the Motorola car phone, relieved to see a full charge. I punched in the number and held up the heavy, corded receiver.

Brrring. Brrring. Brrring.

The phone sounded in my ear.

"We have her here, now," Larry, the lead detective, said when he answered. "Before you say anything, I know you just landed. Your office told me. But we waited for you. This might be the last crack we get at her. So far, no lawyer. She hasn't asked for one. I don't know how long it will stay that way. Can you get down here?" He had hardly taken a breath.

My husband, Marc, looked at me quizzically. Mom distracted Joshua with a game of patty cake. I heard Larry shuffle some papers.

"Doc, we need your scientific expertise. You know these files better than anybody."

"Okay," I said. "I don't have anything with me. Do you have my final report?"

"Of course, and we got dibs on a parking space out front. A patrol guy is guarding it."

"Oh, get some snacks for my family and a place for them to wait." Larry had a wife and daughter of his own. I trusted he knew what to do.

Ending the call, I explained the need to reroute to the police station. Marc sighed. Mom harrumphed. Joshua sucked his pacifier. I redirected Marc to drive past the Irving Park exit on the Kennedy that would have taken us home. They were disappointed; we had been looking forward to hot showers and the comfort of our beds.

Larry, a seasoned homicide detective, and I had investigated Deborah Gedzius for nearly a year. We poured over thousands of pages spanning a 15-year period—hospital records, autopsy reports, witness statements, and affidavits. Between our meetings, we worked on our own, verifying data, re-interviewing people, and filling in the gaps. I studied photos, enlarged prints, and made charts of all the medical information. No detail was irrelevant as we confirmed addresses, times, and the weather. The work had led to this interview.

An hour and a half after deplaning, I sat across from Deborah.

She stared at me; her blue eyes boring into mine. Dyed blonde hair hooded her brow. Larry and his partner, both dressed in plainclothes, flanked her on either side at a casual distance. The four of us sat in hard plastic chairs forming a circle. Oriented in a boy/girl/boy/girl arrangement, we might have been ready for a party game of musical chairs. The only music we heard were the drunk and disorderlies being processed nearby. It seemed loud for the end of the weekend, but then New York didn't have exclusive rights to the moniker, "The city that never sleeps."

Only a few feet away from this woman, I could have leaned toward her and brushed the hair back from her eyes. She could just as easily have slapped me. I supposed that's what the police were there to prevent.

The fluorescent lights cast a blue hue making her lipstick appear bright orange. She wore beaded white, large hoop earrings. "Dolled up," my mother would have said to describe the look. Maybe Deborah had been getting ready for a night out on the town when the police knocked at her door and changed her plans.

Brown roots showed at the crown of her head with light-colored locks pulled into a ponytail. After six pregnancies, carried to full term, she showed a laxity of body. She wore a pastel blouse and stretchy black pants, at least one size too small. I was dressed in a relaxed style too, in brown linen pants and matching top, a bit rumpled from the flight.

Her handbag rested on the floor; contents visible like a messy junk drawer left open. Edges of paper, cellophane, a water bottle, and a pink and green tube of Maybelline's Great Lash. I had one just like it in my purse.

I looked back toward the woman. At 35, she was just a year older than me. Until that moment, I had had no direct contact with Deborah. My experience of her crimes existed in an orderly office or riding with Larry in his meticulously clean car. In the flesh, she was more real to me than the corpses of her babies. Our worlds intersected in this police station.

Nine months earlier I was summoned to my boss' office. As I stood outside his door, I stared at the plaque. Most of the office signs announced an occupation or room's purpose—Investigations or Records. Dr. Stein's read "The Chief Medical Examiner" denoting his singularity and authority. He ran the office since its inception 14 years earlier, in the country's third largest city, and taught forensics for long before that.

I smoothed my hair and straightened my skirt, as if I was back at St. Michael's elementary school awaiting a reprimand from Sister Elizabeth Ann.

"Come in," he said in response to my knock. He gave a friendly smile.

His demeanor put me at ease. He sat at his large oak desk wearing a striped tie and a gray lab jacket embroidered with his name. With his silver-white hair, thick eyebrows, and oversized glasses, he looked like a studious elf. If he stood up, he was only two inches taller than me.

At 75, he and his wife, Elsa, still skied in Austria annually, the country where they met. He performed autopsies once a week. Every morning he walked a mile around the building with security following close behind to keep him safe in this area of escalating crime.

"I need fresh eyes on these old cases," he said. "Someone who wasn't here at the MEO for the original investigations." He pointed to six Bankers Boxes on the floor. "Frankly, I've seen how you work. You're thorough and you'll get it done."

I blushed at the high praise from a man I respected greatly. After training me for a year in fellowship, and elective rotations in my pathology residency before that, he did know me. He'd offered me this full-time position as soon as it opened.

"Work with Larry from Chicago PD. He's the best they got." He continued.

"Of course," I said.

As I started for the door, he said, "How is the little one?"

"He's doing great. Thanks for asking."

Dr. Stein never failed to ask about family. It was a signature kindness.

I probably thanked him for the opportunity, asked more questions: about the cases, policies on documenting my findings, how to report to him, and his expectations. The memory is obscured by the ensuing late nights and weekends studying the files while carrying my full load in morgue work and court appearances.

Even in the depths of research and study, I had not anticipated this interview. My job was to do autopsies, investigations, and determine how and why a person died. I met decedents every day on gurneys in the morgue and occasionally at the scenes where they took their last breaths. I met living people as well—witnesses at accidents, next-of-kin, and lawyers.

It wasn't my forte to question a killer.

The person of interest, the perpetrator of the crime, was left to the police. Law enforcement might ask me to explain my findings to help them sift through the complexity of statements and confessions. I often aided police by analyzing a suspect's comments to determine veracity. I had never spoken directly to a murderer before.

Deborah rested easily in her seat as if waiting to be called for a salon appointment. The only thing missing was a copy of *People* magazine for her to be thumbing through. In 1990, Patrick Swayze or Lady Di might have been on the cover.

She showed less concern than if she was renewing her driver's license. I felt as if I was about to take the most important exam in my life, which had been the forensic pathology boards more than a year earlier.

I shifted in my chair, sitting up straight to project confidence. My family waited somewhere nearby, tired from traveling and wanting to go home. I looked at the top sheet in the file and focused on my questions.

"Tell me what happened the day Daniel died," I said. This two-month-old was found dead in his crib, three years earlier. Larry had advised me to start with the most recent victim. The words felt lumpy in my mouth.

"I don't remember," she said.

As a new mother, I considered finding my child like that and knew the scene would play on an infinite loop. I repressed the desire to retort 'really?'

I flipped through the file and mined my mental Rolodex of information, searching for a question to crack open the vein of answers.

"Is it true that you don't visit the graves anymore?" I said.

Her mouth opened and closed. She turned to Larry's partner, Frank. She crossed and uncrossed her legs and narrowed her eyes at me.

"I enjoy my time with them, but once they're gone…" she said and shrugged. She took an interest in the fingernails of her right hand. They were chewed to the quick with remnants of red polish.

"It must be hard," I said. I let time expand as I nodded my head.

She remained mute.

"Why didn't you want the visiting nurse to help with Daniel? I mean, after all, five of his siblings had died. Did it make you think of your other babies?" I said.

Creases formed around her eyes. Her lips thinned. Her eyes flicked to Larry. He projected nonchalance, a characteristic I had gotten to know well. His worn suit, loosened tie, his very facial expression said, 'Hey you can trust me, I'm a regular guy.' I saw beneath this to the soldier who served in Vietnam, the man who exemplified the motto 'Don't quit.'

"No," she said. "They're just no help. Not them or the monitors, neither."

She referenced the apnea monitors, prescribed by doctors for her fifth and sixth children. They were meant to catch death in the act with an alarm sounding to warn parents their child had stopped breathing. They were no use to Deborah since she never connected them to the babies.

I took another sip of the bitter coffee, then looked directly at her.

"Do you know CPR?" I said.

"Of course," she said.

"When did you learn?"

"After Denise passed." Denise was Deborah's first child, found dead in her crib at five months of age. The name reminded me of another girl, one with unlaced shoes. Had it been popular in the 1970s?

"When was that?"

"1972." She answered that quickly enough.

"Then why didn't you do it when you found Jennifer?" This daughter had been the second infant to die, three years after the first. Deborah was holding the baby when paramedics arrived.

The mother was silent.

"Or for Barbara?" I said. The third infant to die in her crib in 1976.

"My brother did," she said. She sat up straighter. "I didn't need to."

"But your brother wasn't performing CPR when the police arrived; you were holding the baby in your arms."

"It didn't work." She shrugged.

Even the fourth child to die, Jason, a one-year-old boy, did not receive CPR from Deborah.

"They were all crib deaths, you know," she said. "Check it out. You'll see."

That was true. The official certificates of Denise, Jennifer, Barbara, and Jason listed sudden infant death syndrome (SIDS) as the cause of death for each child. SIDS is the unexplained demise of an infant, usually during sleep. Around 3500 occur annually in the US alone. To meet this definition though, the case must be thoroughly investigated.

It is much too easy to smother a baby without leaving a trace.

No one had realized Deborah's children were related until 1980, and the fourth child died. The father's brother had contacted the MEO and said, "I think she's killing them."

That phone call connected the four children to one mother, Deborah. Until then, the infants had been separate cases, pronounced dead on arrival at three different hospitals, all distinct from the ones in which they were born. The children carried unassociated surnames from three biologic fathers. They visited separate pediatricians for well-child checkups. Home addresses ranged from Alsip to Burbank to Chicago—all within Cook County but independent towns. Pre-computerization did not identify that each baby had the same mother. Deborah wasn't forthcoming. Investigative holes swallowed the information.

Then two more children died—Delos Junior in 1984 and Daniel in 1987.

A forensic inquiry began with Delos and intensified with Daniel. Yet there were no leads, witnesses, crucial physical evidence, or a confession. Deborah remained calm. The cases were labeled "Undetermined", a category often reserved for suspicious but unprovable homicides.

Unfortunately, a prevailing scientific theory cast doubt on possible suffocation—infant apnea might run in families. This made forensic pathologists fearful of blaming a parent.

The hypothesis of inherited SIDS would be debunked in 1995 when a mother, the leading example of familial apnea, confessed to suffocating all five of her children. She said their crying drove her to kill.

The investigation of an infant's death was not easy, then, or later. In 2003, the English Court of Appeals issued a ruling in favor of a mother in a wrongful conviction claim. It stated, "Unless the court is sure of guilt, the dreadful possibility remains that a mother already brutally scarred by unexplained deaths of her babies may find herself in prison for life for killing them when she should not be there at all."

Even before this ruling, I agreed with this approach—cautious and careful analysis. The evidence was strong in the Gedzius case.

"Delos was too old for SIDS," I said. "He was two when he died. SIDS only occurs in infants under a year." I took a sip of cold coffee to wet my dry lips. "How did he tear his tongue?"

This showed my familiarity with the details, to get her talking about specific injuries, and what she did to them. As a toddler, Delos would have struggled and been harder to suffocate. The injury in his mouth was evidence of trauma.

"What is the point of all this?" she said. "I answered these questions a long time ago. It's been 18 years since my first baby died. I'm sick of this." She spoke the words smoothly, in an even tone.

"Yes, true, but your husband was murdered last year," Frank said. As Larry's partner, he was investigating this recent crime.

Deborah's husband, Delos, had been shot in the head, execution style, his decomposing body found days later in his apartment. Deborah and he were estranged though she remained the beneficiary on his $100,000 life insurance policy. She was the last person to see him alive. They had eaten out at a fancy restaurant, drank a lot of wine, and discussed how to divide up their joint property—the details recorded on a credit card receipt and overheard conversation. Deborah had admitted to that much.

Death clung to Deborah. Her six children died over the course of 15 years and her husband recently murdered. The word on the street was her boyfriend was a Chicago cop.

She sat calmly, affecting boredom mixed with annoyance. Where was the grief over such an accumulation of loss? The anger at the medical system for not diagnosing her children's problem? The desire for justice for her spouse? Her face told me those emotions didn't exist. Despite the heat in the small room, goosebumps raised on my arms.

I looked over to Frank and then Larry, but they said nothing else. The husband's murder was out of my jurisdiction. I needed to bring the discussion back to the children. Should I ask about the multiple ER visits and the mother's claims that the babies had difficulty breathing or nose bleeds never corroborated by hospital staff? Should I mention the near-death episode of one infant that healthcare workers considered attempted suffocation? Or talk about the neighbor who heard persistent crying from one child minutes before paramedics arrived to find the baby without a pulse or respirations?

After the half-truths and complete lies to pediatricians, nurses, social workers, police, and family, somehow, I was supposed to elicit Deborah's honesty and break the case open; get her to admit what I knew as a forensic scientist that she had done to her babies—smothered them.

If we were in the courtroom, there would be a long wooden table to separate us: me on the witness stand and Deborah at the defense table. A judge could pound the gavel, a bailiff enforce the law, and jurors pass judgment. The police station felt unprotected. Nothing separated me from Deborah except a few feet of air.

The wall clock ticked the minutes—one, two, three. An hour had already passed. The back of my shirt clung to me like Saran Wrap. I gazed at Deborah, and she held my eyes, like in a middle-school staring contest.

I asked her a dozen more questions, going over the circumstances of each of the six children's deaths. Her amnesia became routine. Even simple queries about age or time of year met with "I don't know." Maybe being involved in so many murders blurred the details. Lies distorted memory and, when blended with truth, a warped recall.

"Well, Deborah, thank you for coming in." Larry sighed and stood up. Perhaps he realized the ineffectiveness of the interview or maybe he had too much coffee. The match was over. She had bested us in the eighth round.

Larry did not extend his hand to her as he opened the door. Frank went out first and she followed without saying anything more. I stayed sitting; the effort to stand, a burden. If I tried, I might topple over.

"It's okay, Doc," Larry said, putting his hand on my shoulder. "It was a long shot." His tone was fatherly though he was only 10-years older than me. "Maybe I can find you a snack. Wait here a minute."

I sat staring at the seat Deborah had occupied. Evil needed time to dissipate. Questions and answers repeated in my head. After all the work and the investigation, she was free to go.

Larry returned with a Snickers bar.

"Everybody's good. Your son is playing in the pediatric interview room with your husband, and your mom has made friends with the intake staff," he said.

I smiled—at the resilience of my family, the taste of the candy, and the end of the evening.

Soon after this, Dr. Stein sent a letter to the State's Attorney's Office declaring all the cases to be homicide. The legal system found insufficient evidence. Deborah continued to operate a tavern on the South Side and insisted that this was a "terrible tragedy," and she was the victim of "police persecution."

National cases brought attention back to Deborah from time to time. Chicago prosecutors said they needed more. She was never charged.

About one month after the interview, I discovered I was pregnant with my second son, conceived during the sunny sojourn to Florida. There was a small developing embryo inside me as I spoke with a mother who had murdered all six of her children.

Deborah tallied their deaths like beads on a rosary and contemplated them for less time than it takes to say a single Hail Mary of repentance.

Dr. Stein often quipped, "It's not the dead I fear. I'm afraid of living people."

I understood what he meant.

Cook County

It was 8 a.m. on a Monday at the morgue. Five shooting victims had been brought in since Saturday night. Violence had surged in Chicago in 1990 with at least two killings a day, a majority due to firearms.

The young man's form looked bereft on the gurney. The multiple dissecting stations, overhead surgical lights, and long panels of industrial-sized sinks in the shiny morgue diminished him. At six feet, 185 pounds, he was large for his age of 15 years.

I stood on one side of the corpse; Carl on the other.

"Photos all set?" I said.

"Yup," Carl said.

The brevity of his answer made me look up from writing on my clipboard.

"Anything going on?" I said. "You're usually Chatty Cathy in the morning."

"Nah."

Carl waited for me to make my notes. He had efficiently set everything up: knives, scalpels, forceps on the cutting board atop the stainless-steel table, open-mouthed containers and blood vials labeled with the boy's name and case number, and brown butcher paper on another table waiting for the clothing. Carl fidgeted with the empty and still-clean organ pan. It clanged, metal on metal against the table.

"Seriously, what's up?" I said.

"Guy is the spitting image of my cousin," Carl said.

"That's rough."

I looked at Carl, his head down, rearranging the instruments. This was a hazard in our line of work. Seeing the dead whose appearance, age, name, or circumstance touched us unexpectedly and broke down the ability to separate them from the living.

I leaned over the deceased and placed my gloved hand on Carl's gowned arm. "If you want to step down, I'll wait for one of the other techs."

Doctors and assistants kept consistent partnerships. Carl and I had been hired about the same time three years earlier. We were like step-siblings, raised in our own families but now sharing the same one.

"No, it's okay," he said. "Might never do another case if I went down that road."

Carl and I were used to separating ourselves from the dead. Entering the morgue every day, cutting up human beings, reaching into their heads and chests, holding their hearts, livers, and brains in our hands, required that.

When a corpse looked familiar, it disrupted the barrier.

The teen on my gurney had a kindly face without a beard or mustache. I felt no stubble. "Soft as a baby's bottom," my mother would have said. I didn't detect any aroma to indicate he had shaved.

He wore his hair in a high-top fade. A barber had taken care with the cut; a clean edge marked the neckline. I opened the eyelids. His brown eyes glistened warmly. Not enough time had passed to start the postmortem clouding. What had those eyes seen?

I worked my way along his body from head to toe. The first gunshot wound I saw dotted the side of his neck with a dried line of blood extending to his shoulder.

His clothes dwarfed him. On his torso, he sported an oversized navy-blue t-shirt. When Carl maneuvered the body up on its side, I counted four entrance wounds from bullets on the back. Acid-washed jeans, straight-legged, with rips at the knees (real, not fashionable), covered his legs. The pockets had been pulled out as if to dry on a clothesline. A cop had searched for identification and a weapon at the scene.

The teen wore light-colored boxers, the inside tag reading Fruit of the Loom size 34. An Adidas sneaker over a white crew sock adorned his right foot. On the left foot, a tag with the decedent's name and case number hung from a wire around the great toe. A sock laid across this ankle. The other sneaker sat between his legs. I looked at the soles, clean and almost new.

Carl had arranged the x-rays of the boy on mounted light boxes. Spots of white amidst the gray tissue of the neck, chest, abdomen, and arm denoted lead from the bullets. Projectiles broke his humerus, spine, and ribs, hitting blood vessels, heart, lungs, and liver along the way.

Carl noticed me counting and waited until I finished.

"Hey Doc, did you see this one?" Carl said. I hadn't gotten to that side yet.

I lifted the right upper limb revealing two holes—one in the biceps and one in the triceps. The bullet traveled straight through the arm, spending only enough time to fracture the bone. It wasn't with the body or seen on the x-rays; it probably lay on the ground at the scene of the shooting.

This teen was shot six times.

I read the summary on the chart: "Found on street. No witnesses. No weapon. No one in custody." The day felt daunting.

So much needed to be done: spreading out the clothing for close-up photographs of the bullet holes, examining each perforation for particles of gunpowder, making precise measurements of the skin wounds, using a magnifying glass to check for close-range firing, following the bullet tracks, and recovering the five projectiles still lodged in the body. The clothing, x-rays, and external and internal examinations would be meticulously documented in this homicide case.

Law enforcement would try to link the recovered projectiles with other crimes, matching them with a weapon or a bullet from another case. They would go back to the scene to search for the missing bullet.

"Let's get the probes and plastic forceps," I said.

"Already there," Carl said.

He had done many firearm cases with me and knew the routine. We worked well together, our moves, an intricate choreography. Carl held various body parts and tissues aside while I traced the path of destruction. He exposed the area where the bullet landed while I carefully retrieved the evidence.

"Why plastic forceps, Carl?"

"So as not to damage the bullets. Using metal might scratch the lead. Plastic won't. Cops use markings on the bullets to match it back to a gun."

I admired him as he repeated my impromptu lecture from a previous autopsy.

We spent the next few hours sorting out the order of the shots and the angles, how far away the shooter was when he fired, which wounds were fatal, and whether more than one gun was involved.

My job had steadily become more difficult in Chicago. The number of young black men I met on my table was overwhelming. Disease was not the invader but rather fatal darts that tore through vital organs. A majority were in their 20s, gunned down on the street, an alley, front porch, or car. The number of times each victim was shot increased with each passing year. When I began, my average case had two gunshot wounds, then four and ultimately six. Bigger, badder guns became available on the street. Yet after doing nearly 100 firearm killings, I had only gone to court to testify in a handful of trials. Like this boy's report said, "No witnesses. No weapon."

Carl began stitching the body back up. All the evidence was packaged and ready to sign over to the laboratory and the body fluids bagged for submission to the toxicology lab. Fingerprints had confirmed the decedent's identity.

I removed my personal protective equipment and tossed it into the red-biohazard trash can.

"Thanks," I said. "For sticking around."

"Sure, Dr. J," Carl said as he kept working.

"Are you in the rest of the week?"

"Why?"

"I'm doing cases Wednesday and Friday."

"Good to know." He looked up, pausing with the curved needle pulling the cord taut at the level of the corpse's abdomen. "I'll be right here." He smiled.

Afterwards, I sat at my desk and surveyed the files on top, dozens requiring finishing touches. A box of my personal belongings sat in a corner anticipating an upcoming move.

It had been a difficult search to find jobs for my husband and me in the same city. We were sub-specialized physicians: he a pediatric ophthalmologist and I a forensic pathologist. He was just finishing his fellowship training. We had looked everywhere from Kansas City to Albuquerque to Massachusetts. Often the opportunities were only good for one of us.

A graduate from Marc's training program had settled in Peoria and there was a coroner's system in need of a professional like me. Dr. Kirschner told me that I was stepping off the grid.

I wouldn't miss the daily homicides, the mounting numbers of gunshot wounds that had made me a firearm expert.

I would miss Carl.

Clymer, Baby Girl

My family needed passports. Marc and I planned a trip to Israel, a six-week break before moving to Peoria. This would be the longest vacation since we started medical school more than 10 years earlier. I was pregnant with our second son; Joshua was 18 months old. The whole family would travel to the land of our ancestors, Christian and Jewish. This included my mother.

"Mom, let's go get photos for the application," I said. "Afterwards we can walk over to the post office to file. Maybe grab lunch at the Melrose Diner. We'll take the stroller. It's nearby. Bring your birth certificate."

I checked my hair and outfit in the mirror in our third-floor brownstone. Joshua played at my feet on the living room rug. Light streamed in the tall front windows. The sun promised warmth in the coolness of early spring in Chicago.

"I don't know," she said.

"You don't want to, or you have to look for it or something?" I tried to keep the irritation from my voice. I had the day off, a good time to accomplish errands. The trip was only a few months away.

"I don't have one." This struck me as odd that she didn't have a birth certificate. Then I remembered her adoption. "I have a different card."

She rummaged in her purse and handed me a yellowed four-by-three-inch paper—her name and birthdate written on the front with an official note stating her birth certificate was on file in the Maryland Archives.

"That's fine then. We can just request it from the Bureau of Vital Statistics. Maybe we'll go to the Melrose anyway."

"Okay." She started to take the card back.

"Wait a minute." I walked over to the window for better lighting. Blurred characters lingered beneath the writing. The letters and numbers of her name and birthdate overlay shadows of original information that had been erased incompletely.

Her adopted last name, Ruth, lay atop another. Her birth name, Clymer, peeked out as if afraid to show itself. The year of birth had a number two scrawled over a one making it read "1928"; the original was 1918. My mother went from 62 to 72 years old right in front of me.

"Mom, what does this mean?" I stabbed my finger at the card. "Were you born in 1918?" I raised my voice. Joshua began to cry. "This isn't even a good forgery."

"Shh, you're upsetting him," Mom said.

"Your name is not your name. Your age is not your age. What else have you lied about? Who are you?"

She pursed her lips together and raised her chin like a little kid refusing to take cough medicine. I took Joshua out for a walk.

We didn't speak for the rest of that day. After Marc came home from work, I explained that I was too angry to talk to Mom. He offered to intervene.

He asked her if she remembered the depression of 1929, a reasonable question if she had been 11 years old at the time. She refused to answer. He suggested there might be a mistake on the card and knowing the correct information, would help us get the original. He told her if we couldn't get the official birth certificate, she wouldn't get a passport. This meant no Israel. My mother wanted to go to the Holy Land.

She finally admitted her birth name and date.

Weeks later, when she received her original birth certificate, she wept. The box marked "Illegitimate" was checked. Her mother, Alice Clymer, had given birth to Esther out of wedlock. Perhaps this shame she felt was the reason she hid her birth and adoption.

We took that trip to Israel: Marc, Mom, Joshua, and I with our second son in utero. We strolled cobblestones in Jerusalem, beaches in Tel Aviv, and groves of cedar in a cousin's Kibbutz.

I never forgot about the unexplained lost years of my mother's life.

Part III

Peoria and the Quad Cities

The tightrope
between the morgue and home
stretches taut.

Flies

When it's quiet, you hear them munching and crunching. Hundreds congregate for a feast of decomposing flesh. Still juveniles, maggots eat voraciously during this active phase of their life cycle.

Fly mothers birth eggs in exposed, moist regions of corpses—eyes, mouths, and wounds—appearing as powdery, white specks. Soon though, they become worm-like creatures squirming through multiple growth spurts, discarding pupa casings with each enlargement. Having stealthily entered through sinuses and airways, they feed and excavate brains, stomachs, lungs.

Nature's essential tasks are unseen by most people, who genteelly shoo away a bothersome fly at a cookout. The delicate proboscis searches for a drop of sugar in the remnants of a festive meal. Finely lined wings allow quick escape from the human threatening its livelihood. The blue-green body sparkles in the sunlight.

The beauty of the adult belies its immature state. Fully developed blow flies are pollinators, drawn to the aroma of food or flowers. Their larvae are scavengers of necrotic tissue. Those of us who wield the swatter with murderous venom sense the disgusting childhood of these nuisance bugs.

"I can't get to her," the investigator said, balancing on the concrete ledge of the bridge. He reached out precariously toward a tree rising from the ravine. A second officer held onto the man's ankles. Sweat stained the armpits of their thick police garb.

"Maybe the guys below can push her up," another said.

The body of a young female was suspended upside down in the autumn foliage along this hilly ridge. Red toenails peeked out from the yellow, brown bushes. The sour smell and viridescent color indicated she had been deceased for longer than the 24 hours of unseasonably warm weather.

I had dressed in jeans, a t-shirt, and sneakers, and not my usual hospital scrubs or white lab coat. This was an outdoor homicide scene and rural compared to my big city experience, unlike anything I had dealt with in Chicago, but not unusual for Peoria.

Earlier that morning, a jogger noted dots of crimson in the forest where most of the leaves had already fallen. He slowed, thinking he spotted a downy woodpecker and was shocked to realize it was a woman's pedicure. I had read his statement.

The response team tried to recover the decayed body. It had been dumped headfirst into the trees from the parapet. I stood on the bridge and scanned the landscape to determine the best approach. The slope was steep yet passable.

"Whoa," the officer next to me said after finally grabbing the woman's leg. His gloved hand came away with the fragile skin which draped over the foot like a partially removed sock.

"Wait," I said as the physician in charge. "Forensics 101. Disturb as little as possible."

I descended the gorge to join the downhill team and assess the body from another angle. The head rested 12 inches above us in a tight stand of trunks. Caught in branches, the skull was precariously attached to the neck via strands of sinew, the integument eaten away by maggots. Tugging the body in the direction of the valley might decapitate the woman. We needed to proceed up the slope. The deputies were too big to fit into the narrow space.

"It's up to you, Doc," the lead detective said. "You're the smallest."

I squeezed into the brush. Wedging myself beneath the woman, I stabilized the scalp and yelled to the team on the bridge, "Okay, I've got her."

They pulled. She moved.

Fly larvae landed in my hair and on uncovered arms, showering earthward as we maneuvered the ascent. I closed my mouth and briefly my eyes, so the grubs couldn't get in, my hands occupied with holding the woman steady. The cumbersome retrieval prevented wiping the pests away. A fetid aroma surrounded us.

Step by slow step, we progressed along the uphill grade, preserving evidence, and ultimately reached the roadway. We placed the decedent in a body bag. Maggots wiggled and crawled on my bare skin.

Finishing the transfer, I ripped off gloves and t-shirt, and tossed them onto the road. My torso jumped, a frenzied dance to dislodge insects. My arms flailed, hands swiping at extremities to make sure the writhing critters were gone, a spastic rendition of an MC Hammer song, the finale flipping my long hair to oust anything that remained. Taking a deep breath, I glanced up.

A dozen male law enforcement personnel stood in a semi-circle around me, motionless. Some scrutinized their shoes; others viewed the horizon in the distance; a few boldly stared at my pink lace bra. Despite the warm temperature, my chest shivered, and red patches marked unprotected flesh.

A rookie officer whom I hadn't met before approached, offering a starched shirt on a hanger. He blushed but looked me in the eyes, never wavering with a downward glance at my breasts.

I unbuttoned the uniform and put it on.

Duct Tape

When I arrived at the detached bungalow, there were two cop cars in the driveway. Bobby, the deputy coroner, had called me at home and asked for my assistance. He acted mysteriously, saying only that he needed a forensic pathologist, and not providing any additional information. I had reluctantly left my little baby David, not even a year old yet, sleeping in his crib, while the rest of the family continued their slumber.

Bobby and I were outsiders together in the forensic world of Peoria: he was black, and I was female. I had skipped the usual 20 questions. My neighborhood was less than 10 minutes away from the address.

The vehicles rested quietly without siren or flashes. From the house, lights bled a yellow hue onto the dark street. No crime scene tape marked the property. No neighbors or reporters gathered on the lawn. Already this felt unusual for a suspicious scene, the only kind I was ever called out for by the coroners. I put gloves and booties on as I entered the home.

The chief of police stood at the kitchen counter thumbing through the contents of a handbag. He regarded the wallet and pulled the driver's license out of a sleeve. He wasn't wearing gloves. He didn't greet me.

A single clean glass, plate, and fork rested in the drainboard. The lid to the trash bin was open but without a garbage smell. The back door was closed. The living room looked orderly.

"Who is that?" I said quietly to Bobby pointing to an older woman sitting in a nearby chair.

"The neighbor who found the body," he said.

"Can someone escort her outside? She shouldn't be here." I kept my voice sotto voce. This directive should have come from law enforcement in charge of the scene.

"I agree." Bobby tapped the closest officer's shoulder, "Can you see this lady home? If we have more questions when the doctor finishes, we'll call her."

The woman looked grateful to leave as the policeman helped her to her feet and led her outside.

Another officer talked on the phone in the front hallway and one hovered near the back porch. Bobby stood in the bedroom doorway, like a bouncer at a nightclub.

Everything felt off.

I looked past Bobby. The legs of an elderly woman hung off the bed with her feet on the floor. She lay along the short side of the mattress, as if she had sat down on its edge to rest a moment and then collapsed backwards. A pillow obscured her face. That concerned me.

"I don't know why he bothered to call you out, Doc," the chief finally said, reminding me of his presence. "What is all the fuss?" Waving his hand over the counter, he added, "Look at all these pills."

He had lined up five medication bottles of varying sizes. That didn't seem like a lot to me for an 82-year-old woman.

I ran through the list of procedural errors. A witness sat in the middle of the crime scene. The chief of police handled evidence without gloves. A cop used the telephone. How many people had been in and out of the bedroom obscuring footprints or adding trace evidence?

At least Bobby knew what he was doing. He had seen all of this when he arrived and then called me.

"I photographed the scene already," Bobby said, then turned to the chief. "Can we proceed?"

"Yeah, we're all done," the chief said.

I entered the bedroom. Six feet away from the decedent a stepladder rested against the wall. Above it, an overhead cupboard door was ajar.

"What's in there?" I said.

"A jewelry box," the chief said. "She was putting something away."

Bobby frowned. I shook my head.

On the bed, the woman wore a nightgown with the bottom hem pulled above her knees. Her thighs splayed open. She wore no panties. I moved the pillow aside. Her face was deeply purple. Hemorrhages stippled the whites of her eyes. Using my fingers, I examined the mouth. The frenulum, the delicate tissue that extends from the upper lip to the gum, was torn, indicating direct pressure against her mouth.

Her arms lay straight at her sides. Silver duct tape wrapped tightly around her left wrist with a thick gathering of it on one side creating a pocket. A sticky residue persisted on the skin of the right wrist. The hands had been bound together and then wrenched apart.

"This is why you called me," I said to Bobby. He nodded. If it had been natural causes, he wouldn't need my expertise.

"She's been tied up and smothered," I said loud enough for the chief to hear me. "Her wrists were bound together. She has injuries in her mouth and tell-tale signs in her eyes. She may have been raped, too, but I'll be able to tell you more after the autopsy."

"Whoa, wait a minute," the chief said, coming to stand in the bedroom door. "What are you talking about? There's no forced entry to the house, no signs of a struggle. She even has five dollars in her purse. Besides, her next-door neighbor didn't hear anything all night." He took a breath and shook his head. "C'mon Doc, don't go off on a wild goose chase."

My face reddened.

He explained his theory of a stroke or heart attack. The elderly woman had fallen back onto the bed with the pillow in her hands while suffering a life-threatening natural event. This caused self-suffocation.

I turned to Bobby and mouthed "What the fuck?" Out loud I said, "What about the duct tape?"

The chief paused, but then he smiled, pleased with himself. "Maybe that's where she kept her pill bottle."

"Taped to her wrist?" I said trying to keep from snorting.

"Pretty convenient, right?"

"It would make the bottle hard to open, one handed. And it wouldn't be comfortable stuck on her skin. Besides, with all those medications, which one do you think she would choose?"

The chief wasn't listening; he had finished his duty. He seemed determined to report this as a natural death no matter what I said.

Bobby and I prepared the body for transport to the morgue.

In the autopsy room, I worked meticulously on Frances: documenting her injuries, collecting swabs for a sexual assault kit, carefully removing the duct tape, and securing the irregular edges. I saved all the evidence for laboratory analysis.

The skin on both wrists had been rubbed raw where she struggled against her bindings. The injuries on her face showed she had been smothered. I ruled the case a homicide. The coroner agreed with me.

The police refused to accept these rulings. They concluded the woman died of natural causes. There was no further investigation. I never understood their reticence.

Three months later, the ex-girlfriend of Frances' part-time handyman came to the police station. She brought a ring that her old beau had given her. After their break-up, she felt guilty having this possession. She told the police he had stolen it from Frances.

This prompted a search warrant for the handyman's house. A roll of duct tape was found and secured into evidence. At the FBI laboratory, technicians compared the suspect roll with the tape I had recovered from the dead woman's wrist. Microscopic analysis of the torn ends revealed a matching interlocked pattern. The tape wrapped around Frances' wrists had been torn from the roll at the suspect's home.

The man was found guilty of murder and went to prison.

The Farmer

The aroma of mildew and the sour tang of blood assailed me. A man was face down on the gurney, having arrived in the same position in which his body was found.

"How long did you say he was out there?" I asked my assistant, Paul, who had unzipped the body bag.

"Two weeks. The 15-year-old son found his father that way," Paul said, waving his hand over the man's corpse. "At least that's what the coroner told me."

The body, brought in from a county more than 40 miles away, had been reduced to a clothed skeleton. Dark, curly hair remained loosely attached to dried and hardened scalp. Silt and mud covered the hands, feet, and head. I doubted the timeline.

My duties in Central Illinois were considerably different than those in Cook County. In the Chicago ME system, I had both investigative and autopsy responsibilities but here I served as a physician performing the dissections. Coroners ran the inquiries, often without medical or forensic training, using law enforcement to provide scene information. I wasn't used to this piecemeal approach, or the formal inquests held to vote on my results.

However, I was busier than ever. As the only forensic pathologist in River City serving a 20-county coroner's region, I was in high demand.

Paul picked up the camera and photographed the body with a time-stamp that documented arrival at our morgue.

A heavy long-sleeve shirt and denim pants clothed the dead man. Overdressed, if he was out in the midday summer sun but appropriate for the cooler evenings in August.

As if reading my thought, Paul said "The man usually went out every morning to check on the crops. The corn was blunted from the drought. Maybe he was worried about the harvest and did a check at night."

"Where, exactly, was the body?" I said.

Paul held up a single Polaroid. "See for yourself."

White bordered the photo. A case number was handwritten at the bottom. The man lay face down in a ditch at the edge of a cornfield, the gully full of murky water. A Remington rifle was near his feet. In the background field, the husks were brown, yellow with only a few green interspersed. Owning 350 acres of corn would make this a depressing site for the farmer. It was a brutal summer with daily highs in the nineties, well above the norm, and a relative humidity that made the air feel over 100 degrees. I had spent a lot of time with my boys, David, two, and Joshua, four, enjoying the cool water of the sprinkler.

The autopsy room felt sweltering. Our facility was the embalming suite of a funeral home. The air conditioning had only been turned on a few minutes ago when Paul and I arrived.

"Two weeks you said?" I asked.

"Yup. The boy saw his father on the day he left for Bible Camp and found the body on the day he got back." Paul began putting x-rays up on the light box.

It usually took a few months to turn a dead human being into a skeleton. For this man, it had been much less. The severe weather and location had accelerated the decomposition. In the water-filled ditch and high temperatures, the flesh steamed off leaving only sinew and bone. The sturdy clothing kept the bones together.

"What's the verdict from the coroner?" I said.

"Suicide."

We stared at the x-rays. The chest and abdominal films lit up with meteoric streams of lead fragments, characteristic of rifles. Two distinct wound tracks were visible showing the farmer had been shot twice, not typical of people who shoot themselves.

"Whoa," Paul said. "Got to rethink that."

The quiet settled around me as Paul crossed his arms over his burly form, looking like Grizzly Adams, the nickname my boys had given him. Paul had years of experience as a hunter.

I put on surgical gloves and helped him roll the body face up. Not much was left of the skin. The eyeballs had collapsed into deflated sacs. A strip of unshaven skin marked the area above the mouth. Cigarette-yellowed teeth appeared larger than normal due to the absence of the lips. The head, the most frequently chosen site for suicides, had no gunshot wounds.

As we angled the body to remove the clothing, a fragment of bullet dropped from the shirt, pinging on the metal table. I saw an exit wound in the front of the shirt; the fabric characteristically ripped outward.

Paul took more pictures. He knew what to do at each step of the case: paperwork, prep, photos, x-rays, labs, dissection, clean-up. Having trained at a large Medical Examiner's Office, he was an experienced and knowledgeable technician. I had recruited him to Peoria.

"Here," Paul said, holding up a second bullet. A large Caterpillar belt buckle had stopped its egress.

The farmer had been shot twice, both times in the back.

I picked up the magnifying glass and examined the clothing, finding the entrances and the exits of the gunshots. There was no soot or powder deposition to indicate that the weapon was fired any closer than three feet. Laboratory ballistics testing would later confirm this. I noted the rib fractures followed the path of the bullets from back to front. I walked between the body, the clothing, and the x-rays confirming the tracks of the wounds.

We retrieved the bullets and metal fragments. Paul was adept with the detailed procedure, so important in presenting evidence in the courtroom. We signed our initials and dated the envelopes. State police would later match the bullets to the weapon that fired it, the rifle found at the man's feet.

"Not a suicide," I said.

"I thought not," Paul said.

It took many weeks to sort out what had happened in the corn field. Each interview with the 15-year-old son resulted in a different version of the event. The trooper called me after each session, and we discussed the plausibility of the boy's stories.

At first, the teen said he didn't know what happened to his father who had been fine when the boy left for Summer Bible Camp. He really had gone away to camp; there were many witnesses to his presence at prayer circles, craft activities, and daily sports games. Yet the teen remained the last person to see the farmer alive.

Then he said his father was depressed and hadn't been acting right lately. The dates and times of when he last saw his father kept changing. The boy eventually conceded to being there when the shots were fired.

The teen claimed the two had struggled when he wanted to go hunting and the man tried to stop him. The rifle accidentally discharged. I told the trooper the shots weren't fired at close range grappling for the weapon.

Then the boy insisted he shot his father in self-defense. The two had argued and the man lunged at his son, so the teen panicked and shot him. I told the trooper that the farmer had been shot twice in the back.

Eventually, the youth admitted to the shooting but excused his action by declaring long-term abuse. Investigators could not corroborate this after many interviews with teachers, social workers, and family members, but it's a common enough accusation in patricide.

The son was charged with murder, tried, and sentenced.

The rifle belonged to the teen, a Christmas present from his father.

THAT KID

I channeled what my mentor had taught me as I sat rigid on the witness stand. In training, when I had asked Dr. Kirschner how he handled the tough cross-examinations, he said, “Remember, you’re the doctor.”

As I stared at the attorney who was expecting my answer, that advice didn’t feel helpful.

“Can you answer the question or not?” she said. She stood behind the defense table and gripped the edge.

The courtroom was quiet, just a few observers: attorneys, defendants, and me. There was no jury; this was a bench trial decided by the judge.

“I don’t know,” I said.

“You don’t know? It’s a yes or a no, Doctor.”

Her line of questioning had taken an abrupt departure from the case. I was testifying in the trial of a care facility charged with medical negligence. I had autopsied an elderly woman and determined she died from sepsis due to untreated bed sores: open and gaping on her back allowing bacteria to spread to her blood, and her organs to shut down.

“Can you repeat the question?” I said. I had no problem remembering what had been asked. This was my signal for trouble. I expected the prosecutor who had brought me in as an expert witness to take notice and object. She did not.

“Okay, Doctor.” The defense attorney smiled. “Isn’t it possible for someone to have a widespread infection and a caretaker not to recognize the severity?”

She was the lawyer for the middle-aged couple who ran the home. They claimed they never saw a single bed sore on the woman. At autopsy the wound cavity was deep, down to bone over the sacrum and putrefying. The defense theory seemed to be that anyone could miss this obvious life-threatening infection, including licensed caregivers.

Experience taught me not to engage attorneys in hypothetical battles. The lawyer had asked if someone could miss a massive infection and not recognize how bad it was. The question was overgeneralized and didn't deal with the facts of the case. Details were missing—the when, what, how, where—of the situation. When I expressed a professional opinion in a death, I relied on all the data. Hypotheticals conveniently left facts out.

"I don't know," I said. "In what circumstance? Where was the inciting injury? Was it visible? What type of infection? Who was the caregiver? Who was the patient? Could they express discomfort?"

My questions streamed like a magician pulling endless handkerchiefs from the mouth. Still, no one objected.

"I need comprehensive information to form an opinion," I said and looked at the prosecution hoping that they recognized this vague and broad line of questioning should be invalid.

Attorneys and physicians often spoke different languages. Lawyers dealt in rare possibilities; medical examiners dealt in credible probabilities.

The defense attorney's smile didn't falter. She leaned further forward toward the witness stand; her eyes bore into me.

"Okay, let's get specific," she said. "You took your son to the hospital yesterday because he had an unrecognized infection, isn't that true?"

At the mention of my youngest son, David, tears filled my eyes and threatened to spill down my cheeks. Her outline blurred. No one had ever mentioned my family in a court of law.

"You missed his infection, didn't you, Doctor?" she said, more loudly.

I stopped breathing. I turned to the judge.

"I need to use the bathroom," I said. I had never cried on the witness stand or had any excuse to interrupt my testimony.

"Objection," said the prosecutor, a beat too late. It sounded like she was objecting to my need for the bathroom.

I hurried from the courtroom not waiting for the judge's reply. The door banged behind me. I sat on the toilet in the ladies' room in my gray-suede suit. My head dropped to my knees.

I had spent the previous day and night with my three-year-old son, David, at the hospital. He had an overwhelming infection in his hand requiring emergency surgery and intravenous antibiotics.

"Dr. J?" The prosecutor stood outside the stall.

"How did she know?" I said.

"When we delayed the trial yesterday, I told her why," she said. "I never thought she would bring it up in court."

"I am not going back in there. She had no right, no right at all." My sobs continued.

"She was out of line. I'll have a sidebar and explain to the judge. We have a 15-minute break. Come back when you're ready."

I felt violated. My personal life used against me in the hallowed halls of justice. What did my son have to do with this?

I felt guilt, too.

It had begun with a childhood accident. Marc and the boys were out flying kites on a sunny October day while I was at work. My husband brought scissors to untangle the monofilament string. Marc exclaimed to the kids how beautiful the crimson diamond-shape looked in the sky.

Joshua cut the grass and nearly amputated his brother's left little finger as David reached down to take a turn. The Joyce Chen scissors were strong enough to cut chicken bone but lightweight and easy to handle, even for a five-year-old.

David screamed and ran toward his father; his left hand covered in red. Marc told me later that he was disoriented and thought David held the kite. Joshua was crying, rapidly breathing with the beginnings of an asthma attack. As Marc moved closer, he recognized the trauma and pulled off his sweatshirt to make a tourniquet. Grabbing both kids around the waists, he managed to carry them to the car, then rushed to the hospital. He didn't call me until everybody had settled in the ER.

That had been nearly a week ago. A hand surgeon reattached the finger that had been dangling by a tendril of skin. A sturdy plaster of Paris cast covered my little boy's hand; the protective wrapping obscured the fingers. The bandaging safeguarded the delicate microsurgery. No one could see the pinkie finger.

David was a real-life Curious George. After the injury, he dropped an apple in a toilet and retrieved it with his bandaged hand. He kept this a secret, only telling us after the complications that followed.

It was Halloween and we readied for trick or treating. David claimed this was his favorite Jewish holiday. That year he played the role of a pirate, a recycled costume of his older brother. In a photo, he appears jaunty with a black eyepatch, and red and white striped shirt, fringed at the waist and cuffs. His cast shows the wear and tear of a toddler.

In retrospect, he is flushed and his face a little puffy.

The next morning, Namma, as the boys affectionately called my mother, and I rushed around getting the kids dressed and giving them breakfast. As I pulled the pajama shirt over David's head, his skin felt hot. Quickly I palpated the lymph nodes in his left armpit, swollen to the size of grapes. Medical alarms rang in my head. His finger must have a serious infection and it spread to his body. The covering on his hand precluded me checking his digit.

"Mom," I said from the bedroom. "I have to take David to the emergency room. His finger is infected."

Namma ran up the stairs at my call. "Okay, Mary, I'll take Joshie to school."

"Thanks."

"Where are we going?" said David, not sounding like his exuberant self.

"The emergency room. The doctor needs to take the cast off and check your hand. You have a little fever."

"Yea," he said, eternally the optimist, focusing on the word 'off' and freedom for his hand.

At the hospital, doctors removed the cast. His little finger looked like a rotting Bob Evans pork link. The surgeon took my son to the operating room and debrided (cleaned up) the wound and rewrapped it. He couldn't tell me if the original microsurgery was harmed or not. David received heavy doses of multiple antibiotics.

That had been 24 hours earlier. With hardly any sleep I had headed straight to court.

I went back to the courtroom. The prosecutor had discussed the matter with the defense and the judge. There were no more questions about my son or allusions to my ignorance as a caretaker. I was probably on the stand only another few minutes.

The delay in seeking care for David's hand weighed heavily upon me.

Marc, Namma, and I rotated shifts at the hospital with David. Within a week, after two more surgeries, my son was back at home. He had a Broviac catheter in his chest to receive double antibiotics three times a day through its intravenous port directly into his heart. I did all the treatments at home, using sterile technique, masks, and gloves. David had to mask up, too, since the line lay just inches from his face.

This aggressive regimen treated bacteria that had gone deep into his bone. The doctors hoped to avoid amputation. The therapy also involved weekly blood draws to check David's white blood cell count and any signs of continuing infection. This lasted for three months.

Surrounded by IV poles and bags of fluid medication, I relished the time snuggled next to David. We listened to audiocassette recordings of children's books, the kind that beep to signal when to turn the page. David loved the sound and action of the stories. Our favorite was *Plants of Peril* featuring Batman and Poison Ivy. The beautiful villainess escaped Gotham Penitentiary on the first page but ended up captured by Batman and returned to her cell in the end. Maybe it was an allegory for wanting freedom yet needing structure. I held David close.

On the final day of blood testing, David refused to get out of the car. No amount of explaining, bargaining, or pleading had any effect. Finally, I had to carry him into the clinic. He squirmed and cried.

The pediatric nurse, familiar with toddlers, deftly took him from my arms. I followed them into the treatment room. Two staff members placed him onto the examination table and harnessed him with thick leather straps, like something out of *One Flew Over the Cuckoo's Nest*. The room decorations belied this with primary-color clowns cavorting on the walls. Afterwards we went home in a somber mood.

A few days later, David had his last medical visit with the Infectious Disease specialist. The months of intravenous antibiotic therapy were over. Lab results had normalized. The doctor removed the chest catheter. As the physician filled out paperwork, I tilted David's face up to mine to give him a kiss. I froze.

"What is in your nose?" I said.

David put his right index finger to his left nostril.

I bent his head further back and looked. A yellow fuse bead winked at me.

"David," I said.

He looked chagrined. I swallowed.

"Doctor," I said, my voice quavering. "We have a new problem."

I explained that my son had stuck a bead up his nose, the polyethylene kind used to make a design on pegboard to be heated and made permanent. The kids had brought their creations home from school recently: a duck and a smiley face. The beads were safe for children, made of food-grade material, but not meant for insertion into noses.

"We'll have to call ENT and take him over there. Maybe they can remove it as an outpatient procedure. Otherwise, he'll have to go to the ER," the doctor said. He gathered David's file.

"Wait," I said. "Do you have a hemostat? Can't you just take it out? I can see it clearly."

"Oh, no, no, no." He backed away. "I'm not that kind of specialist."

We looked at each other. David sat unusually still on the exam table.

Seeing the yellow bead emboldened me despite his reluctance. "Do you have a hemostat? Just get me one."

The doctor reached into a nearby drawer and retrieved a sterilely packaged instrument.

"Gloves." I spoke to the doctor as if he were my assistant. "Shine your penlight here."

I put on the surgical gloves and opened the package of the hemostat. In less than a second, I had the bead out with no bleeding.

"Thanks, Mommy," David said. "It hurt."

Belt Buckle

"WHAT's that up ahead, Silo?" The farmer spoke to the Border Collie at his side.

Pale blue lined the sky at the horizon. His early morning ritual included feeding the chickens, putting the cows to pasture, and surveying his crops. Smoke rose from a spot 100 yards away above the corn stalks. He walked slowly toward it. Silo barked as they approached.

The chassis of a subcompact rested against the trunk of a white oak tree that marked the edge of the farmer's property. Heat shimmered from the tangle of metal even at 15 feet away. He trudged back to the house to call the troopers.

Sergeant Jones documented everything the farmer told him and took pictures of the accident scene. I read this information in the call sheet.

A charred, wet body lay on my autopsy table. Firefighters had pulled it from the driver's seat after they doused the wreckage with water. The gas tank had ruptured on impact, a known hazard with Pintos. The driver sat in his seat burning for hours. The wreck was still hot when the first responders arrived.

I looked at the body, mostly a skeleton. Tiny patches of singed hair clung to the back of the head. The face had lost the eyes, ears, and nose. Teeth appeared large with the lips gone. The surrounding skull with a patina of soot and lace-like cracks looked like a prop from a Día de los Muertos celebration.

Fragments of seatbelt adhered to the front of the ribs; the material more durable than skin. The arms posed in a boxer's form, known as a pugilistic attitude in forensics: muscles tightened with heat and the flexors, bulkier than the extensors, pulled the forearms up. He looked as if he wanted to punch me in the nose except that he was missing his fingers. The fragile digits might have fallen off during recovery of the body or else burned away, making fingerprints impossible to obtain.

I wasn't even positive it was a man. The remnants of clothing and size of the bones made the choice probable. A clue lay at the waist: a large oval belt buckle, the kind cowboys wore in Western movies. I wiped it with a cloth revealing "Savanna, Illinois, A Sportsman's Paradise." A menagerie of deer, bass, and pheasant rose out of the center. He must have been a hunter.

I put his age in the late twenties judging by the pattern of cranial sutures on the top of the head. Over a lifetime, skull bones knit together in a certain order, fusing completely in different decades.

"Do we have a tentative?" I said to Paul, referring to the identification of the corpse.

"Yup, owner of the car," Paul said.

With this body beyond visual recognition, I needed to compare antemortem and postmortem dental or medical records to give him a name. In the early 90s, DNA wasn't a common scientific method, at least not in this neck of the woods in the Quad cities of Illinois and Iowa.

Paul rested on a stool at the side of the small room. Earlier he had put up the x-rays, taken photographs, and lined up specimen cups on the cutting board along with knives that he sharpened for me in every case. He took pride in his job skills. I appreciated his professionalism. His jocular banter was a bonus, but it was absent that day.

I raised my eyebrows. "Do you recognize the name?"

"No, I don't." He paused so long I thought he was done speaking. "Just that's it's the middle of the night, all by his lonesome." Another pause. "Big ole' bonfire."

The ghost conflagration flickered around us, and I almost felt the heat of the flames.

Brrring. Brrring. Brrring.

Paul deftly removed one glove and picked up the receiver on the wall.

"Hell-o," he said. "Yeah, she's right here."

He stretched the cord to me, holding the handset against my ear.

The coroner talked at me. I tried a few times to interject but he plowed forward.

"Look, it was the guy's car. There was no one else in the auto. He was in the driver's seat for Chrissakes. The girlfriend identified the belt buckle. Just sign the death certificate." The coroner said this like a military commander giving orders.

I listened to the dial tone in my ear. The coroner hung up without even a response from me.

I had transitioned from a high-powered position in Chicago, where I worked with a dozen other board-certified specialists, to being the only forensic pathologist in central Illinois. I tried to bring the local investigation system into the 20th century even as we headed into the 21st. Every day I asked the coroner for what I considered essentials for my work: x-rays, toxicology testing, a scale to weigh the organs, and photographs from the scene.

My predecessor, a general practitioner with little pathology training, took 15 minutes to do an autopsy compared to my 90-minute average. He incised the chest, opened the ribs, grabbed the heart, and made cuts in the coronary arteries. I had seen this. My method of a head-to-toe examination inside and out took longer and required more tools and tests, especially in suspicious deaths.

If the coroner had stayed on the phone, I could have explained the forensic necessity to do a proper ID. The body was burned beyond recognition. No distinct features remained. Other people might sport that buckle. Someone might have borrowed the car. When I worked in Chicago, a scientific identification would have been required.

I took off my gloves and dialed the coroner back.

He picked up on the first ring.

"Good, I..." he started.

I interrupted. It was my turn to talk quickly. "Herb, I need the dental records for this man. I can't do the identification without them. I'll be at the morgue another two hours. That should give you enough time to send someone over to Morton." The small town was 15 minutes away. The car was registered to the man at an address there.

"Just sign the DC, Mary."

"No."

I heard him breathing heavily, indicative of his decades of smoking. I stayed silent like in a game of Be Quiet: first person to speak, loses.

Technically he was my boss. I worked for him as the coroner's physician.

I stared at the shape on the table, recognizable as human only by general form and remnants of clothing. His hair, face, smile, voice, and stance unique to him were irretrievable. Only the teeth persevered so I would use them to link back to the man's living self.

"Herb," I said finally. "It won't take you but a half hour. I know you don't want me to list the guy as a John Doe on the death certificate, but I will if I can't officially confirm him." This unfortunately would have ramifications for the family: insurance, the estate, and closure. I didn't want them to suffer but I was sure the coroner didn't either. He was an elected official.

He hung up.

Paul and I worked for two hours on the man, collecting evidence, blood for toxicology, and a complete dissection of internal organs. Blunt trauma from the crash killed him, not the fire. He had not inhaled any smoke into his lungs.

As we finished up, the sergeant came through the door.

"Got something for you, Doctor," he said, handing me an envelope.

I pulled the radiographs from the Morton dentist out of the package and put them up on the light box. Distinctive fillings shone on the antemortem x-rays matching white spots in the teeth on the decedent's postmortem films. I had my formal identification.

The dead man reclaimed his name.

B.I.T.C.H.

Tick. Tick. Tick. Tick.

The clock's second hand made its way to the hour of 4:00. I had been waiting 90 minutes in this windowless room, seated on a metal folding chair. The overhead panel lighting cast a yellowish glow over the papers on the table in front of me. The fluorescence bothered my eyes. I looked over the 10 pages more than five times and memorized them. This was my habit when testifying as an expert witness.

The top sheet listed Cause of Death = Multiple Blunt Force Injuries and the Manner of Death = Homicide—along with a summary of the autopsy findings. These generic words did not describe the beating and sexual assault the young woman had suffered before she died.

I smoothed out my blue, knee-length skirt and adjusted my matching suit jacket. This outfit was not as comfortable as the surgical scrubs I wore just an hour earlier. The taupe pantyhose felt tight, and my feet pinched by seldom-worn dress shoes.

Pushing bangs out of my eyes, I looked up as the door to the small witness room opened. The bailiff put his head in saying, "Doctor, they're ready for you."

He opened the tall, heavy wooden door leading into the courtroom and motioned me ahead of him. I walked down the aisle to the witness stand, past four rows of long mahogany pews on either side. The gate in the middle of the balustrade separated the public from the official area and grated loudly in the hushed atmosphere. Some observers coughed and rustled jackets. Two university students doing internships in my office sat in the front row to attend their first murder trial. Newspaper reporters and friends of the accused filled out the remaining seats.

There were two long tables just past the gate. Identical 30-somethings in blue-pinstripe suits representing the State sat at one. At the other were two men comprising the defense team. One was paunchy and mustachioed. His pale-yellow shirt, matching the sickly color of his skin, had creases from recent packaging as if the price tag had just been removed. The other man had salt and pepper and wore tailored tan slacks with a navy-blue jacket.

A black-robed, white-haired judge sat in a high leather chair behind a raised oversized desk. He was a caricature of the role, serious and aging. Flags, their fabric in folds, hung from tall poles on either side of him—to the left, American and to the right, the state of Illinois.

Thirteen individuals representing a jury of the defendant's peers were seated in two rows of swivel chairs off to one side of the room. The air felt stale like in a transatlantic airplane cabin.

I climbed the two steps up to the witness box, still below the level of the judge. He looked toward me and smiled.

"Do you read Patricia Cornwell?" he whispered conspiratorially. He referred to the former journalist turned popular novelist who featured a female chief medical examiner as her protagonist. The writing was bloody, like the job, and Scarpetta, like me, was never able to wash it off.

"Yes," I answered truthfully, though I wasn't under oath yet.

"Do you like her?"

"She's awesome." I really did like her books. We conversed in a low tone meant only for the two of us.

"Is it realistic?"

I considered the implications of the question. At a cocktail party, I might expound on the topic but here there was only a moment to get it right.

"She takes liberties for the sake of the plot, but she's done a fantastic job portraying Dr. Scarpetta."

He nodded, then banged the gavel.

The bailiff announced, "Court is now back in session. The honorable Steven Simmons presiding."

After placing my left hand on the Bible, I raised my right hand.

"Do you swear to tell the truth, the whole truth, and nothing but the truth, so help you God?" the bailiff said.

Despite the separation of church and state guaranteed in the constitution, this archaic procedure persisted. This use of the Christian holy book made me uncomfortable. Lying under oath was against the law—perjury, a felony. That should have been enough.

The first part of my testimony was monotonous, but I had it down to a patter, describing the credentials that qualified me to be an expert in forensic pathology. Looking at each juror to connect and humanize myself, I named my high school, college, and medical school, and the hospitals in which I'd trained.

"Doctor, please describe, if you will, the injuries which caused Amy's death," one of the matching prosecutors asked.

I detailed the wounds on the victim's head, face, chest, and extremities. There were extensive bruises, large lacerations, and broken bones. I gave measurements of size and shape. Injuries on her hands and forearms showed that she had struggled with her attacker. She was raped and sodomized. Then to obscure the evidence, she had been run over by a car.

The prosecutor put a poster-sized photograph of the decedent's head on an easel in front of the jurors.

"Not simply a car accident, then?" the prosecutor said.

Before I could answer, the dapper defense attorney was out of his seat, saying, "Objection."

I had learned from Dr. Kirschner to hold my answer until the court ruled on the admissibility of the question. The man accused of the crime claimed he ran over a drunk woman lying in the road and then fled the scene.

"Overruled," the judge decided, which meant I could answer the question.

"But your Honor," the opposing lawyer said.

"Counselor," the judge chastised in the voice of a mother scolding a misbehaving child. "This is an expert witness and may express her professional opinion. Doctor, please answer the question."

"No. Not a car accident," I said.

The prosecutor strode back to the table and conferred with his partner.

"Just to be clear, Doctor, Amy did not die as the result of a hit and run accident?"

"Objection." Opposing counsel was out of his seat again.

"Overruled," the judge said, more quickly this time.

"That is correct. She did not die as the result of a hit and run accident." I repeated the phrase.

"That is all, your Honor," the prosecutor said.

The defense attorney studied his handwritten notes. He rose and slowly approached the witness stand.

"Good afternoon, Mrs. Jumbelic," he said, smiling broadly.

I counted to five in my mind to avoid showing annoyance at this lack of respect. Not being addressed as "Doctor" in this setting was an insult and a deliberate tactic to diminish my testimony.

"Now, you describe the wounds on the head, but these could just as easily be from a minor car collision, is that correct?" he asked as he raised his eyebrows.

"No, they couldn't," I said.

"And how are you so sure of that?" He scoffed and waggled his head as he spoke.

"There is a classic depression in the skull caused by a heavy object forcibly striking the head." I was in my medical element now. "The injuries that killed her were due to direct blows to her skull."

"Wait, these wounds you describe could be from a car running her over, correct?" He had a bright gleam in his eye as if he stood under sparkling lights. He turned to face the jury and gave a confident nod before he looked back at me.

Very slowly I responded, "There is indication she was run over but only after she was beaten to death with a weapon."

"Yes, or no?" he said sternly.

"Yes or no, what? What is the question?" I wanted him to be exact with his language.

The other prosecutor was on his feet, "Badgering the witness, your Honor."

"Ask a question, Counselor," the judge directed his words to the defense lawyer.

The attorney looked miffed but changed topics. "You testified earlier under questioning by the State that this woman had sexual injuries to her vagina and anus?"

"Yes," I said.

"Have you seen these pictures from the scene where her body was found?" He held up several glossy shots.

"Yes."

"Your honor, I would like to mark these as exhibits 21, 22, and 23."

The judge looked over at the twin prosecutors.

"We have no objection," they said.

The defense attorney handed the prints to me for review. I took my time, noting the deserted alley, the dawn appearing at the edges of the film, the oddly twisted body sprawled in the middle of the roadway.

"Do you see the rocks in exhibit 21?" he said.

"Yes," I said.

"Here is exhibit 22, this is a close-up view of one of the rocks in the previous photograph, correct?"

"Yes."

"And here is 23, showing an even closer view, correct?"

"Yes."

"Isn't it possible, Mrs. Jumbelic, that this woman, drunk and stumbling, sat down hard," he emphasized this word as if he had just sat down on something sharp, "and the rock itself caused the injuries in the vagina and the anus?"

I focused on the photographs. The rocks had sharp and blunt edges and were strewn at the side of the road. No blood dotted their surface. The lawyer was trying to distance the defendant from the violent rape committed on this woman before she was killed.

Keeping my face neutral, I said, "No."

"But look at these rocks." He jabbed a finger at the largest rock, a jagged piece of limestone about six inches at its widest point.

I sat calmly, waiting for a query, and continued to look at the picture as instructed.

"Well? Can't you answer this simple question?"

The black-robed figure banged his gavel, startling the courtroom. "Counselors, approach the bench."

Both teams of lawyers gathered around the high desk as if summoned to the boss's office. Only the defendant remained at the table, looking down at his hands in his lap. He appeared vulnerable and weak in this sanitized setting without a hint of the brutal rage from the night of the murder. The conference at the bench continued in indistinct whispers. As they headed back to their established positions, my questioner slumped.

"Why couldn't the wounds on her genitalia be caused by inadvertent contact with the rocks?" he said.

This was an opening I'd been waiting for to expound on the scientific evidence.

"Because there are no tears in the clothing, though she's been redressed with her underwear on backwards. Furthermore, there is no blood on the rocks and no transfer of soil or dirt to her wounds."

His face flushed. He flipped the pages of his yellow notepad noisily. I could almost smell his feverish odor. A loud scratching of someone crossing and uncrossing their legs in synthetic pants sounded in the quiet space.

"No further questions," he finally said.

The judge nodded to me and said, "You may step down."

Heading toward the exit through the observer section, I signaled to my students that it was time to go. We convened in the main hall and headed toward the elevator.

"Can you believe that?" one of them blurted out.

"Believe what?" I said. The freshman who had just spoken stared at me wide-eyed, his face quite pink.

"Well," he said, visibly nervous as he glanced at his colleague, a sophomore, for reassurance. "Well." He seemed doubtful about continuing. I waited, anticipating a legal conundrum I could solve.

"Did you hear what that defense attorney said?" he finally said.

"You mean, what prompted the sidebar?" I said.

"No, no, after that, when you were walking out of the courtroom." He blushed.

"No, what did he say?"

The student looked at his co-intern for support and she whispered, "Tell her."

I smiled encouragingly. "Go on. Tell me."

"That attorney turned his back on the court, and to the whole audience called you a bitch." They awaited my reaction.

I'd been called worse. Frustrated coroners, police detectives and prison guards cursed me behind my back and even to my face when they disagreed with my tactics or conclusions. My reputation was as a tenacious, aggressive female. However, this statement in so august a setting surprised me.

"Did he now?" I gave a full-throated chuckle.

The interns gazed in bewilderment.

The woman said, "Dr. J?"

"That's great," I said. We stopped in front of the elevator. "Okay, let me explain. I've worked long and hard for that title. It's a compliment."

"A compliment?" the woman said defiantly.

"You saw how the defense attorney treated me in there?"

They nodded.

"Calling me Mrs. and not Dr., trying to diminish my testimony? Sometimes there is no civility even in this arena. Have you ever heard the acronym B.I.T.C.H.?"

"No," they chorused, shaking their heads.

"The letters stand for Boys, I'm taking charge here," I said.

They smiled with this explanation.

Ten years later a statue of Abraham Lincoln would be erected in front of this courthouse. I have always tried to live by his words: "Be sure you put your feet in the right place, then stand firm."

Sometimes that makes me a bitch.

The Scream

"Come on, honey," I said to Joshua, as I zipped up his parka.

His kindergarten teacher had called two hours earlier. My son had a fever. I brought him back to the office with me. Namma picked up his younger brother, David, at about the same time from the Montessori Learning Center. Joshua had napped on the waiting room sofa while I did paperwork.

Working later than intended, I was in a hurry to get home. Snow swirled under the dim bare bulb outside my office. Only two days before Christmas, the usual traffic was absent; staff had gone home early. My coat flapped in the wind. Shivering, I pulled the door closed and locked it.

Joshua dragged his heels as we headed to the car. A cough sounded from deep within his chest, worrying the doctor in me about his asthma. We headed to the dark parking lot with one stanchion light illuminating the boundary.

"You can ride up front today, buddy," I said as I nudged him towards the station wagon. This would allow me to keep an eye on his breathing.

He waited at the forward passenger door while I fumbled for the car keys. Case files and presents encumbered my arms. My purse strap dropped from my shoulder to mid-arm, unbalancing my parcels.

In the shadow of an eave, a burly shape distracted me; why was the custodian working at this hour?

In an instant, we were face to face. The man was not the super. He was not anyone I knew. He slammed me against the car, shoving something hard against my ribs. His breath was sour; his hair brushed my forehead. We were close enough to kiss.

"Don't scream or I'll shoot," he whispered.

A primal shriek filled the air. I had emitted it despite his admonition. I dropped forcibly to the ground, landing hard on my knees. Teeth banged together from the impact. The robber deftly lifted my handbag from among papers and packages flung in an arc around our feet.

Dream-like images played in a split-second in my mind, a re-enactment of the last moments of hundreds of my patients, a vivid hallucination of the weapon firing, the fatal injury, and my own death:

> Asphalt dusted by fresh snow.
> Blood pumped from a severed aorta.
> Skin paled like Snow White.
> Numbness and cold advanced.
> Bullet traversed fabric, tissue, metal.
> Fired gunpowder scented the air.

He didn't shoot. The thief turned, pocketbook in hand, leaving me alive on the blacktop.

Scrambling to the other side of the car, on my hands and knees to avoid being a target, I reached my son. I yanked Joshua down to the ground with me. Sensing my panic, he began to cry, breathing in gasps and wheezes. I ran my hands quickly over him—no trauma. Then I cried.

We crawled back to the building, the armed mugger's whereabouts unknown. After unlocking the door, and hurrying inside, I dialed 9-1-1. We sat huddled on the floor.

"He flew, Mommy," Joshua said, "like Superman." He took some ragged breaths.

The robber must have looked mammoth to my son, trench coat billowing, as he hurdled a chain link fence to escape.

My knees were raw, stockings torn open. Pink saliva dripped from the corner of my mouth. I had bitten my lip in the fall.

"You're bleeding," Joshua said.

"We're ok," I said, reassuring myself by patting my body—no gunshot wounds.

"Was that a bad man?"

"Yes, Joshie."

"Will the police catch him?"

"I hope so."

"Why did you scream?" He sobbed anew.

I brushed the hair out of his face. He felt feverish.

"I wanted to warn someone about what was happening," I said. Throughout my career, I had seen too many victims who remained silent.

"But nobody heard you, Mommy," he said. He looked at me, eyes luminous through his tears.

"The most important person of all heard," I said, bending to kiss his head. "You."

That night, at bedtime, I held Joshua close as we sat in the rocking chair in my bedroom, a gift from my mother when he was born. It had been a long time since I held him like that. An hour earlier, when we entered the bedroom, he started crying. He was afraid of the dark beyond the window.

Our pale reflections looked ghostly in the glass. I lowered the blinds and drew the curtains.

Usually, I read to both boys, one snuggled on each side in the crook of my arms. As I turned the pages, they would sometimes read along. Favorites included *Chicka-chicka Boom Boom, Corduroy*, and anything by Dr. Seuss. Lately we had enjoyed E. B. White's tales of mice, swans, and pigs. Some nights I invented stories about a little boy named Petey and his friend, Elfin-Nelfin, who went on grand adventures in the sky and underwater meeting magical folk.

That night I just held Joshua. Namma laid down with David to read. I could hear him laugh as Namma said in a deep voice, "You must not hop on Pop."

"Where's the bad man, Mommy?" Joshua said.

"The police are looking for him, honey," I said. I didn't tell him I had little hope of the culprit being found. These were the same officers who had investigated the duct tape murder.

"Why are you crying, Mommy?"

"That man took something important from us." It wasn't my purse, wallet, or anything tangible that I cared about. My son's innocence was gone.

Joshua looked at me then put his head on my chest and wrapped his arms tight around me.

Six months later, we moved to central New York, for a better professional opportunity for me. I would get to be a Medical Examiner again, no more struggle as a Coroner's Physician. Like in the previous two moves, I was pregnant, this time with my third son.

Even after our Goldilocks' move to Syracuse (Chicago, too big, Peoria, too small), it took years to assuage Joshua's nighttime fear of windows.

I always closed the curtains.

Stryker Saw

Dots of perspiration gathered around my industrial safety glasses. Overhead lights glimmered, reflecting on the stainless steel of the table. Heat emanated in waves; the air humid despite the air-conditioning.

A butcher's apron lay heavily at my neck and covered my surgical scrubs. The waistband felt tied too tightly. Privacy-glass windows, along one wall, above my head, revealed the dark of night outside.

I adjusted the surgical lamp to focus on my dead patient's chest. My pathology assistant turned on the Stryker saw. Louder and more piercing than a dentist's drill, it had taken me years to get used to that buzzing sound, like a symphony of colossal bees, especially when more than one tool was operating.

The Stryker was efficient in its purpose. An oscillating metal blade cut through hardened material without harming underlying soft tissue. Developed by an orthopedic surgeon in the 1940s for removing casts after broken bones healed, it had a unique application in the field of forensic pathology for the autopsy examination.

During the autopsy, we used scalpels to dissect the skin, fat, and muscles of the chest, revealing the sternum and ribs beneath. Then we used the Stryker to open the thorax. The whirling blade sliced easily through the cartilage connections, smoother than cutting through bone. This provided a safe approach.

The old-fashioned method used mammoth pruning shears. They had unwieldy handles, nearly a yard-long, making it hard to get a grip to pull them together. These ancient scissors transected the ribs making a crunch as each bone fractured. They created a wide field for dissection but produced sharp spicules that could puncture the dissector's skin. Going through the cartilage with the Stryker, closer to the center of the chest, gave a smaller area through which to enter the body, but the remaining nubs couldn't hurt you. It was faster, too.

The technician was doing the preparation for toxicology testing; the blood would be analyzed for drugs and poisons. He used a 50-ml syringe with a three-inch needle. The apparatus looked like a prop from *Frankenstein*. When he finished, I gripped thc slippery heart, the size of a cantaloupe, in my left hand, while with a scalpel in my right, I cut its attachments to the body. Blood spilled out, two pints, leaking from all the major vessels.

That's when the corpse spoke to me.

"What are you doing?" the man said, wide-eyed and frightened. "I need that."

"Oh," I said, not as surprised as I should have been. I called out to my assistant, "Can we put this back?" This conversation felt completely logical.

The strident ringing from the Stryker began anew. I was not using the saw, and apparently the technician wasn't either. We were the only people in the room, except for the talking corpse. Still, the saw spun its blades insistently, louder. The resonance intensified.

The alarm clock read 20 minutes past six. The reverberations of its bells clamored for my attention. Hitting the off button, for the final time, after two snoozes, I swung my legs to the side of the bed and sat up. The horror film slid away as my surroundings came into focus. The bedroom windows leaked pale dawn into the room.

My ungloved hands were empty: no blood, no heart. The blankets and my nightgown twisted around my waist, entangling me. I kicked at the bedding to free myself. The aroma of brewed coffee, on an automatic timer, beckoned me to the morning.

The nightmare isn't the same every time. Sometimes I'm holding the brain, with the patient's skull opened à la *Hannibal*, while we converse.

In the worst of the dreams, my own body lies on the autopsy table in the limbo between life and death and I am requesting a vital organ be returned to me.

It took me years to pluck up the courage to ask a coworker if he ever had these kinds of visions; the positive answer made me feel less lonely.

Still, the fear of slicing into a living person haunts me.

Part IV

Syracuse

I want to stop
and smell the roses;
the dead get in the way.

Home

OPENING the wrapping, I saw two severed arms in the package. Their pale white skin speckled with tiny yellow bumps. Chipped coral polish, inexpertly applied, was visible on the fingernails, bitten to the quick. An aroma of astringent emanated from the limbs along with a sour smell. The scene felt surreal for my first week back at work following maternity leave for my third son.

"Where were these found?" I asked the young cop, who shifted back and forth, breathing out puffs of winter air.

He pointed to a white pickup truck with the passenger door hanging open, parked in an otherwise empty lot. The vehicle gave the impression that someone had just run in to buy a pack of smokes at a corner store. A large hand-made sign at one edge of the property advertised real estate for sale. The red spray paint on the wooden notice was stark against the snowy backdrop. The truck at 50 feet away had a coating of white powder covering the hood.

Two teenage boys stood near the front of the vehicle, heads bowed, kicking the slush on the asphalt with their sneakers. A suited, middle-aged man leaned into the conversation, putting his hand on the taller boy's shoulder. I recognized the Syracuse detective. The teen recoiled at the touch and shook his head vigorously. The youths appeared to be denying everything.

"Was that the condition of the car when you got here?" I returned my attention to the young cop.

"I didn't touch anything. Not even this," he said nervously, looking down at the partially opened parcel laying at our feet.

"I know," I said.

He nodded, comforted by my tone.

I used a different approach, "When was this body found?"

Glancing at his spiral notebook, he replied, "2200, Doctor." He looked earnestly at me, waiting. It was already over an hour later, past 11 p.m. The patrolman had been standing outside guarding the remains. He looked cold.

"Anything else turn up yet?" I said, squatting down to take a closer look. The arms were only partially exposed, but clearly detached from the rest of the person. There would be a whole lot more of a body out there somewhere.

"No, sorry. We're waiting on the search warrant." He stomped his feet to warm them up.

The young cop filled me in on the basics. The boys had broken into the pickup and stole a package wedged under the front seat. Having carried it to an adjacent alley, they used a pocketknife to open their treasure. It was tough work getting through butcher paper and multiple layers of heavy plastic wrapping until they exposed what was inside. The shock of it made one of the kids lose his macaroni and cheese dinner. It congealed near my feet emitting the aroma of vomit.

What did they think they were going to be rewarded with on this cold February night? Booze? Drugs? Something more basic—food, clothes? The result of this juvenile prank traumatized them with an emotional retrograde amnesia. The event, as they repeatedly recalled to investigators, started with them opening the container; they couldn't reconstruct the timeline backwards from then.

One boy kept saying, "When I cut it, the hand just fell out." He repeated this phrase as a mantra to any question posed to him.

The teens' naivete and sincerity were the only things preventing the police from considering them suspects in the murder.

The detective finished with the youths and walked quickly over to me blowing on his ungloved fingers. Despite the chill in the air, he looked flushed.

"What have we got here, Doc? White girl, right? Teenager?" he said. He spoke quickly, anxious for my reply.

"I don't know." I hesitated. "I can't really see the details of the skin. It appears pale but…" My voice trailed off.

Only a cursory exam was possible here at the scene. Not wanting to supply erroneous information, I used caution determining the age, gender, and ethnicity. Advanced microscopic and radiologic analyses would help me make those conclusions.

"I need better lighting. I'll know more when we get to the morgue," I said.

At first glance, the arms did appear to be from a young person, but x-rays would show growth plates in the bones, distinctive markers for age. The diminutive nature of the hand and the nail polish suggested a female. Looking at tissue cells under the microscope, not in this dimly lit street, would reveal gender and ancestry.

"Okay, I get it, but the chief is ready to move on this. Could be it's that missing girl from the next county."

"Maybe."

A young blonde girl had been missing for nearly two years. There were posters all over the region—at throughway rest stops, convenience stores, post offices. Her face was well known. Yet, there must be dozens of other girls who were missing from Central New York and beyond.

My initial observation was that the limbs had been preserved for a long time.

"Can you get me any reports from the past 10 years on missing teens in the area?" I said.

"10 years? No way that those have been out here that long."

"Sure, not in the truck. But they look like they were stored somewhere, maybe for quite a while. Someone might be mobilizing them now." My words sounded bizarre even to me. Who cut up a person, used fixatives, meticulously swathed them, then left them in a box in their truck?

"Yeah, whatever, we'll get you what you need." The detective turned to his sedan, leaving the patrolman and me to wait for the transport vehicle.

The rest of the examination of these two lonely body parts took place in the bright autopsy suite. My technician and I carefully processed the wrapping. The perpetrator might have left a trace hair, fiber, or fingerprint behind. There were so many layers of plastic and paper to go through before the arms themselves were inspected. Surgical instruments and a dissecting microscope assisted me in the evidence collection.

What had looked like Caucasian skin at the scene, was not. It is only on the surface that skin color is displayed. The underlying layer, the dermis, is white in everybody. When I stretched the arm open, darker cutaneous clumps appeared at the elbow creases. On these arms, most of the pigment was denuded. Histologic slides confirmed the extensive melanin deposition of an African American. Radiographs of the humerus and radius revealed the person to be approximately 12 to 17 years old. Additional studies proved the limbs were from a female: someone's daughter, sister, grandchild, niece.

A long night and another day passed before I faxed my summary over to the police department describing the severed upper extremities. The limbs originated from an African American girl, and it appeared as if she had been dead quite a while. Hack marks were noted at the amputation site of the long bones of the arms near the shoulders. These saw wounds were postmortem; she had died before this barbarous act. Bits of soil had been trapped in the coverings indicating she was in the ground at some point. The remainder of her body was still unaccounted for.

It was my responsibility to name this girl. To do this, I needed to know who she might be. No supercomputer existed to quickly assign an individual's identification.

After I telephoned the police station, the desk sergeant transferred me to the records clerk who passed it onto the lead detective. I asked about missing African American teenagers from anywhere in the area.

"There are none," the detective said.

Then the police chief assured me personally: no black female teenagers were missing in the city or county.

Where had my victim come from? Where was she going? How did she end up as a discarded sack in a truck?

Police located the owner of the vehicle. A search of his residence uncovered more, but not all, body parts; each parcel wrapped in precisely the same method and well-hidden on the property. The girl's head and thorax were never found.

This case made the news with the gruesome allure of tragedy. Luckily, this reporting led to an interview with a distraught man claiming that the victim was his granddaughter. He described that she was last seen in the company of the suspect, who had been a neighbor. This young girl had been missing for five years. The police captain was quoted in the paper as saying "there is no way" these remains could be this teenager. This bold statement shocked me.

I called the lead detective.

"Doc," he said as he picked up the phone.

"My case, could it be Qiana?" I asked. Before this newspaper article, there were no possibilities, no missing girls.

"Well, Doc, the body doesn't look like it could have been there all those years."

Inhale, exhale, then speak, my inner self cautioned.

"Forensically, I've determined that she could have been there that long. It's in my report. That I sent over. A preservative was used. She was buried in the ground at some point."

A pause ensued as he considered the information. "But Qiana was never really missing." He sounded like he hoped to end the discussion.

"What do you mean she wasn't really missing? The grandfather said she's been gone since she was 12—that's five years. You never gave me any records for missing black girls. He said he filed a report."

The detective didn't answer right away; maybe he hadn't heard me. I was about to speak when he responded in a quiet tone. "They were considered runaways. Not missing kids."

They. More than just one overlooked report.

Stunned by this news, I hung up without further word. My stomach roiled at this blatant racism. Ultimately, a multi-agency meeting would establish that three missing Syracuse girls fit the profile for the victim at my morgue.

Frank McCavey had been listed on the newspaper byline. I talked with him about his conversation with the grandfather. Tracking down this relation of the missing girl took me one step closer to her identity. When I telephoned, the granddad gratefully told me Qiana's story—her troubled youth, friendship with this older man, the family's pain, and years of loss.

The scientific identification took a long time, not the immediate results seen in television crime shows. In government work, the medical examiner's office competes with other agencies for precious tax dollars—fire safety, police surveillance, social services—an unending list of protectors and caregivers for the living. The dead, particularly the long dead, held a lower priority.

The tissue had severely degraded and required specialized DNA testing. The analysis used the girl's mother's genes from a cellular organelle (the mitochondria) and compared them with the victim's. A federal agency agreed to do the specialized testing for free, but we had to wait in a long line.

Speaking with the family every few weeks, I kept them updated on the progress. Qiana had broken her forearm as a kid and the victim had healed bones in the same spot. Everything seemed to indicate that it was Qiana who lay in pieces in my morgue. Still, science needed to officially confirm her identity.

Finally, all the remains—the arms, thigh, pelvis, and leg—were linked by DNA to this missing teenager. As devastating as this was to the family, they expressed gratitude to me for letting them know what happened to Qiana, for caring about who she was. More than a year after the gruesome discovery in a deserted parking lot, they held a memorial service for their little girl.

On the day of the funeral, I met Qiana's grandfather at the front of the white clapboard church. We went into the sanctuary where a simple, large wooden cross adorned the altar. No figure of Christ rested on it, only slats of wood. The grandfather handed me an elementary school photo of Qiana secured by yellowing tape onto a piece of cardboard with crayoned decoration around it. The child in the picture grinned widely with a missing front tooth. Her yellow top had a plaid Peter Pan collar. Small red barrettes decorated her short, black hair. Tears welled up in my eyes. Her grandfather leaned in to hug me as I clung to the photo like an amulet.

With a dignified nod he headed to the front of the church, as I slipped into a seat in the back pew. A mournful tune sounded on the upright piano while the family and congregants filed in. Everyone was dressed in matching hats, gloves, ties, and breast-pocket-liners. The reverend began with the 23rd Psalm, as quiet weeping could be heard in the background. A semi-circle of votive candles flickered on each side of the altar.

Then, as if signaling an end to the mourning, the music crescendoed and the choir, dressed in white surplices, began singing. People rose to their feet with energy and enthusiasm. My heart pounded with the rhythm of the clapping. The row of supplicants in front of me moved side to side. Neighbors in my pew rocked against my shoulders, too.

"And upon the streets of glory, when we reach the other shore, and have safely crossed the Jordan's rolling tide." The entire church sang and pulsed with life.

Hands rose in the air with the next lines, "You will find me shouting 'Glory' just outside my mansion door, where I'm living on the hallelujah side."

My cyes drifted up watching the swaying arms as the heat from the crowd made wavy lines in my vision. I imagined the body parts coming back together to form a whole, no longer a lost little girl, but one with a name and a family, and finally going home.

GREEN STUFF

"MOMMY, what's that green stuff?" David, my kindergartener, said as he pointed to his little brother's mouth.

It was a September morning, after Labor Day, and the first day of elementary school for my two older boys. I stood at the open door checking to see if the kids needed sweaters. A breeze blew back my hair; the air registered at room temperature, perfect with no humidity.

The bus was scheduled to be here in 20 minutes. My husband had left for work an hour earlier. I had been hurrying around the kitchen, zipping backpacks, and preparing lunches. I would soon be headed off, too, to the Medical Examiner's Office.

Our family had grown to six—Marc, me, Namma, and three sons.

Marty, my youngest at 10 months old, sat on the floor of the pantry, smiling widely as drool resembling chlorophyll dripped from his mouth. I rushed to him. My fingers swept over his tongue and teeth extracting pea-sized crumbles. I picked him up. He squirmed as I held him a little too tightly.

The source of the dribble became apparent as I scanned the pantry. Empty boxes for recycling were pulled away from the wall. A mouse trap lay on its side. Scattered green pellets like buckshot littered the floor. I envisioned the sequence of events in the same way I reconstructed scenes every day. Marty had pulled the cardboard away, shaken the bait like a rattle toy, picked up the colorful pebbles, and put them in his mouth.

"Joshua, call Poison Control," I instructed my eldest. At eight, the son of a forensic pathologist, he knew where the emergency telephone number was. "Tell them a baby ate some mouse poison."

I knew the pathogenic properties of the substance used to kill small rodents. The bait acted as an anticoagulant causing internal bleeding. It didn't happen rapidly and only a small amount was lethal for a mouse. I didn't know what quantity might make Marty sick.

Was this a case for Ipecac to induce vomiting? Or should that be avoided? Was it basic or acidic? Should I give him milk or water? I didn't have the manufacturer's original data sheet for the poison. More importantly, my textbook, *Medical Toxicology: Diagnosis and Treatment of Human Poisoning*, was on my bookshelf at the office. I used it extensively when evaluating fatal cases due to toxins and chemicals.

My mother paled and stopped pouring a cup of coffee for me. She hurried over to us.

"Sweetie, are you okay?" she said to her youngest grandchild. Marty laughed in response.

Mom went to David at the breakfast counter and rubbed his back, in need of providing comfort to someone.

"The phone isn't working," Joshua said. He handed me the landline receiver—no dial tone. We couldn't use my cell phone either. Service in our area was spotty in 1996 and limited to the street.

"Go over to Miss Teddy's and call poison control from there." I directed him to our next-door neighbor, 83 years old and steadfast. She would be calm in a crisis.

Marty's good mood continued with Namma, David, and me focusing on him. I reassured myself that experts would clear up my concerns quickly.

Within minutes, sirens wailed in the neighborhood. Miss Teddy had called 9-1-1 and not the 1-800 number I advised. She activated all the emergency services when she reported a child was poisoned.

The doorbell rang. David ran to the door. Two EMTs came in, along with a police officer, and two members of the fire and rescue squad. One had on protective gear for a possible hazardous material exposure. My mother offered them coffee.

One of the men, taller than the others, was suited in yellow with tactical belts and harnesses crisscrossing his chest and waist. His eyes scanned the large kitchen. Half-eaten waffles sat on plates, syrup and butter congealed in their crevices. Condensation dotted the bottle of milk. Unfinished peanut butter and jelly sandwiches lined the cutting board. Slices of MacIntosh apples were nearby, slowly browning in Ziploc enclosures. Paper bags marked with "Josh" and "Dave" waited to be filled with lunches. Backpacks rested by the door; they contained new composition books and pencil cases.

A giggle erupted from Marty as he reached past me to the man with the face shield. He opened and closed his tiny fist. Flecks of green powder lined the creases of his palm. I grabbed his hand and brushed the harmful crumbs against my dress. I didn't want him to put his hand in his mouth again.

David grinned at the crowd. The uniformed men stared at David.

"Are you alright, son?" the tall man said. He seemed to be in charge.

"Yes sir," David said.

I groaned.

The right side of David's face was swollen; the eye almost completely shut. Pink and red discoloration encircled his forehead and cheek. My incessantly inquisitive middle child had tangled with a bee's nest the day before. After icing and Benadryl in the evening, I had convinced myself it looked better this morning. In the harsh overhead lights, it seemed worse.

"What happened to your eye?" The tall man crouched to an even level with my son.

"A bee stung me. It might have been a hundred of them." He sounded proud of his adventure. His eye closed completely when he smiled.

The officer straightened up. Joshua slammed the front door and ran into the kitchen.

"Mom, Miss Teddy made the call," he said. "I couldn't stop her. I told her to call the other number, but she just wouldn't listen." The words rapid-fired into the crowded room. Joshua's right big toe stuck out of a hole in his sock after running outside without shoes.

The men's eyes turned to my oldest son holding a portable phone in his hand. Joshua went over and replaced it in its cradle. A loud dial tone erupted as he hit the speaker button.

"I swear the phone wasn't working before," I said.

"What happened here?" The tall man fixed his gaze on me.

My face flushed.

"My son ate mouse poison." I saw the officer swivel toward David. "Not that one. This one." I jiggled Marty on my hip.

He breathed in deeply, then issued commands as he pointed to the responders. "You take the little one, you take the older one, I'll take this one," the tall man said as he triaged the care for my boys. "And you," he said pointing to the police officer, "stay here with mom and grandma."

The pair of EMTs took Marty and sat down on the floor with him. They checked his pulse, respirations, and skin. Marty grabbed one man's hair and pulled him closer for a kiss.

"Stable. Plan to transport. I'll radio in," the second paramedic said.

"I'll go along," my mother said. "Mary, you stay with the other boys." I knew she was right, but I felt sad to be displaced from my baby. I hugged and kissed Marty several times before he was carried to the ambulance. It was only when I was out of sight that he started to cry.

I heard the officer questioning David about injuries, fights, his parents, and his brothers. In another room someone queried Joshua about his family, responsibilities, and living conditions. I knew the routine. Child abuse and neglect cases were part of my work and expertise.

Not much time had passed, less than 10 minutes. It felt interminable. When the interviews were done, everyone convened in the kitchen.

"Thank you, ma'am, we have everything we need," the tall man said, extending his hand to shake mine. As he did, he squinted at me and tilted his head. "You look familiar."

"I'm the Deputy Chief Medical Examiner." Up to this point, I hadn't mentioned my affiliation with Onondaga County Government where I had been working for the past year.

"Oh," he said, blushing. "Well, nice to officially meet you."

"Thank you for your service." It was all I could think to say. I smiled with overexuberance.

The team departed.

"Get your stuff ready for school," I said to the boys, trying to keep the quaver out of my voice.

I gathered lunches and backpacks, wiped hands and faces, and hurried Joshua and David to the street corner, all the while reassuring them that Marty would be completely fine. The bus turned onto our street and stopped. I kissed each boy on the head. The smell of Johnson's Baby Shampoo made me weepy.

"Love you pretty lady, bye bye," they chorused, mimicking a popular cartoon. The bus door wheezed open. They didn't look back.

My heart was racing; I took calming breaths. I went into the house to call the hospital from the now-and-always-had-been-working phone.

The ER physician told me that it would take a lot more than a handful of the poison to cause any problem to a human, even an infant. Marty could have eaten all the pellets in the trap and been fine. He required a shot of Vitamin K and needed follow-up blood tests but was home in an hour. I didn't go to work that day.

Twenty-four years later, Marty and I sat at the dining room table discussing Vitamin K and its clinical uses. He was a second-year medical student, evacuated home due to COVID, and studying for his exams.

"You were given that drug," I said.

"When?" he said.

"When you were a baby and ate mouse poison."

He seemed to consider this, maybe remember the event. I helped him with a recap.

"That makes sense. To help my blood be able to clot." He scrunched up his face. "That was really stupid, Mom."

My eyes welled up—my fault, lack of attention, neglecting my youngest.

"I mean, why did I do that? Didn't it taste bad?" he said.

I reached over the textbooks and academic papers piled on the table and kissed the top of his head.

The Spider

People arrived, in groups of twos and threes, faces anxious. They looked rumpled as if they'd slept in the airport after a canceled flight: hair lackluster, makeup smeared, clothes smelling stale. They spoke in whispers, with an occasional sob. The families of the victims of TWA Flight 800, had come to identify the personal belongings of their loved ones.

Large cafeteria tables displayed dozens of photographs, eight-by-10-inch glossies, laid out one by one showing an assortment of items—a gold wedding band inscribed with initials and a date, a piano charm on a broken silver chain, close-ups of multi-colored tattoos. Investigators had chosen the most unique objects and distinctive skin markings found on the travelers.

I stood at the ready, white lab coat over my blue scrubs. My heart still raced from the journey from the morgue in Suffolk County to this Family Assistance Center near JFK. The state trooper had driven 90 mph on the Long Island Expressway congested with summer traffic creating a lane of his own with sirens, lights, and a depressed accelerator pedal.

This was my first mass disaster, despite more than a decade with the dead. I was almost 40 years old, my birthday two weeks away. The governor had gathered experts from around New York state to help speed up the identification process.

Most of my day had been spent inspecting victims pulled from the Atlantic Ocean off the coast of East Moriches. I had never seen so many dead people in one place. Many of the bodies tore apart on impact when their jet inexplicably fractured in mid-air 12 minutes after take-off and plummeted into the Long Island Sound from 15,000 feet.

At the Family Assistance Center, I watched as relatives circled the table searching for a familiar artifact. A slightly built man leaned close to a photo. Standing alone in an old-fashioned pin-stripe suit, he seemed dressed for a funeral. His hair was black and parted neatly on one side, and he bore a well-groomed mustache.

"Excuse me," I said. "Do you recognize something here?"

"*Scuzzi*," he said. "My English is not so good. *Italiano*?"

"*Español*?" I replied.

He smiled nervously and nodded. He pointed to a photograph.

I picked it up and gestured for him to follow me to a private room. After I closed the door, he reached out and shook my hand.

"Francesco," he said.

"Mary."

"*Doctora*."

He sat on the chair opposite me, looking fixedly at the picture of an upper right arm. From the photo, it was impossible to tell whether the arm was still connected to its body. A simple spider tattoo loomed in the close-up shot so that even the *trichobothria* (leg hairs) were in focus. The tag read #202.

"*Mio fratello*," he said. "*Mi hermano*." My brother.

"*Lo siento*. I'm sorry for your loss," I said. It was a standard phrase, wholly inadequate, but necessary. "Is anyone here with you? *Familia*?"

He shook his head.

"*Fotos de su hermano? Registros médicos y dentales*?" I said. We needed to obtain all medical and dental records to verify the man was his sibling. According to protocol, we couldn't rely solely on his word about this less-than-unique tattoo.

"I come alone to New York. From Roma," Francesco said. The conversation blended Italian, English, and Spanish. "The airline flew me here. After the crash." His eyes teared. "Fifteen years we didn't see each other." Francesco ran a hand through his thinning hair. "Antonio came to America. Francesco," he said pointing to his chest, "*Italia*."

He stood up and removed his suit coat, folding and laying it carefully on the chair, then unbuttoned and rolled up the right sleeve of his shirt. He couldn't get it past his muscular biceps. He took off his vest and then his shirt, arranging them on top of the suit jacket. He looked bereft standing there in his white sleeveless undershirt.

Francesco turned to show me his right deltoid. In the same location as the arm in the photo, he sported an identical three-by-three-inch spider tattoo, complete with spinnerets and eight eyes. The arachnid's once completely black abdomen had faded to dark gray on both the living and the dead men. No other distinguishing inked features appeared—no webs or black widow's hourglass. The skin decorations could have been prison designs, symbols of being trapped, or meant as an ominous warning.

"Me and Tony got them at the same time," he said. "Young men. *Pezzi grossi*. Big shots." He flexed his muscles for emphasis. "*Per favore*." He reached out for the photo. I handed it to him, tears threatening my eyes. He held it up next to his arm to compare. "*Uguale a. Iguale*. Same, same." He began to cry.

There were many questions to ask about Antonio's health, life, parents, and children for comparison DNA testing, part of a complete postmortem interview. There would be time for that. I stood up and hugged Francesco.

"*Tranquilo*," I murmured.

He put his forehead on my shoulder and continued to sob—for his brother, lost years, childhood memories, and the spider tattoo.

The other 228 identifications would have to wait.

Rain

"What's going on?" I asked. Anger edged my voice as I watched the dead being laid on the floor—more than 200—in a cavernous Navy supply shed.

"I don't know, Doc," said Kimo, my pathology assistant, as he put on a butcher's apron. He had trouble tying the belt around himself due to his thick torso.

"Here, let me." I secured the knot. He turned to face me.

"Boss' orders. 'Lay them out', so that's what I'm doing. Something went down with the guys that were here earlier." He was referring to the Korean government officials who met with our commander that afternoon. I had seen the group crammed into the only air-conditioned office at the end of the hangar.

This was my second time working at a mass disaster. My first experience was the TWA plane crash a year earlier. The commander for the federal team had been there assisting and he recruited me to their team.

It had been an exhausting week since Korean Airlines flight 801 crashed into a hillside just outside the airport in Guam. Because Guam is a territory of the United States, Federal teams responded including the one to which I belonged, DMORT—Disaster Mortuary Operational Response Team. When I got the call, I had to search a world map to locate this small Pacific Island.

I sat down on a folding metal chair at the pathology station, defined by blue tarp walls strung on aluminum poles. The autopsy table consisted of a large piece of plywood suspended on two sawhorses. The only instruments—a scalpel, steak knife, and small cutting board—laid on top. There was no running water, or garbage disposal.

Someone had made a signpost, á la *M*A*S*H*, with our team's home cities on it. Mine said "Syracuse 7749 miles;" Kimo's read "Honolulu 3799." Like most of my co-workers, we were far from the familiar, deployed for weeks at a time. Poor cellular reception along with the 12-hour time difference made family phone calls rare.

The passengers had been headed for beach vacations and honeymoons. A majority were South Korean nationals. The remote location of the airplane wreckage made retrieval of the bodies difficult. The Navy Seabees used earth-moving equipment to get to the site while other rescuers descended a ravine on foot to reach the 26 survivors. The dead were brought out by the military in bucket brigade fashion. Now, the bodies were being laid out on the floor of this makeshift morgue.

The rain beat hard on the metal roof, echoing in the vast space. Personnel hurried back and forth between the refrigerated trucks and the building, carrying body bags. The workers became drenched from the storm just walking the 15 feet to do this chore. Though it was August and not yet monsoon season, the downpour remained steady and heavy, like it had been on the night of the crash.

"Do we have to put them on the floor?" I said. Each decedent was being placed two feet from another forming several long lines in the football field-sized room.

"Not enough gurneys," Kimo said.

Traditional forensic identification—fingerprints and dental evaluations—had been going very slowly. Translating Korean records and nomenclature to compare with our postmortem inspections made the process laborious. The next of kin demanded to see their relatives; they didn't care to wait for scientific proof. They formed protest groups outside the secure military entrances and at the airport. Dozens of Asian television stations and newspapers covered the situation. The Korean government insisted the families be allowed to visually identify their loved ones.

Kimo unzipped a body bag and folded the top over to expose the head. Bruises suffused the older man's face, hidden by smeared blood. I walked with my assistant as he continued preparing the others for viewing. A little girl was charred to bone due to the jet fuel fire that had burned for hours. Another woman flung to the edge of the crash displayed pink skin, as if she had taken a dip in a cold lake. She had died from breathing the smoke of the fire. Many corpses were green and bloated, from days in the jungle heat. The coolers helped slow but didn't stop the decomposition process.

The smell of rotting flesh mingled with the odor of burnt tissue, fabric, and plastic. Dried mud, grass, and blood obscured what clothing remained on the cadavers. I felt overwhelmed.

"Are you staying to put them back?" I asked. I referenced the nightly protocol of returning the bodies to the reefers (refrigerated trucks) after we finished our examinations, where they would remain until formally identified and released to a funeral home for transport back to their families.

"Yes. Commander said to give them three hours. Military guys are guarding. I'll go grab some dinner," Kimo said.

Government representatives would bring the families through once the staff left. I had no more work to do that day.

"*Mahalo*," I said.

"*Aloha*."

Holding a thick piece of cardboard over my head, I ran to my rental car and got in. Approaching the large metal gates of the compound, I flashed my badge to the guard, who waved me through.

A winding drive along an access road led to the resort hotel where our team was staying. There was no traffic; my headlights were the only illumination. Water poured onto the windshield faster than the wipers could clear it. Cool air from the defroster chilled me after the heat in the supply shed.

Suddenly, the car hit a bump. I stopped and put the high beams on. Dozens of frogs hopped across the road in front of me. Getting out of the car, I looked back and saw that I had run over several of the little creatures.

I stood there, rain soaking my clothes, and for the first time since I arrived, tears flowed down my face until the only water remaining came from the sky.

PHOTOS

Images shed light onto the past.

Author at three years of age with mother and father, Baltimore, MD, 1959

Author in fifth grade, St. Michael's Elementary, Overlea, MD, 1966

Author with her cousin, Lea Bisconte, Catholic Youth Organization Dance, Baltimore, MD, 1972

Author in Cook County Morgue, Chicago, IL, circa 1987

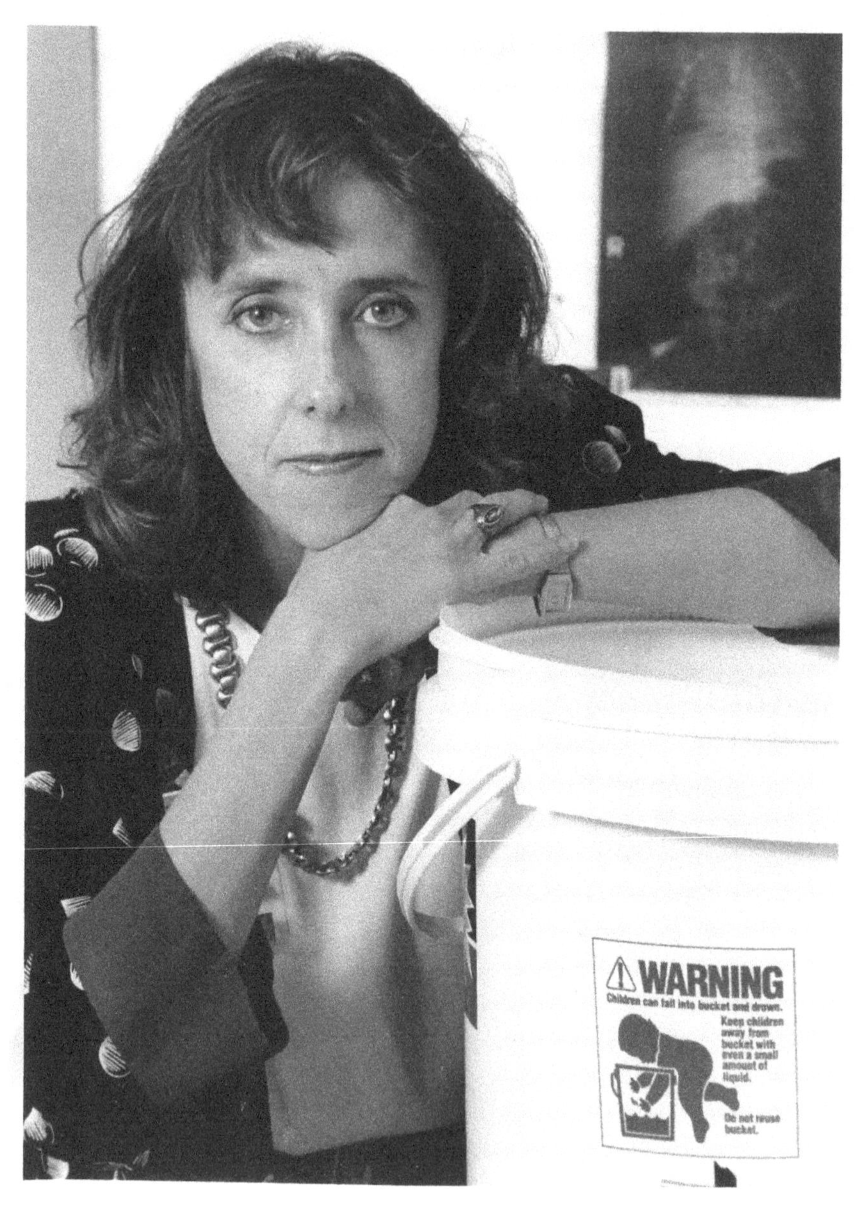

Author in Bucket Warning Campaign, photo by Fred Zwicky for NY Times and Peoria Journal Star, 1992

Author with Connie Chung, Eye-to-Eye, spotlight on Gedzius murders, 1994

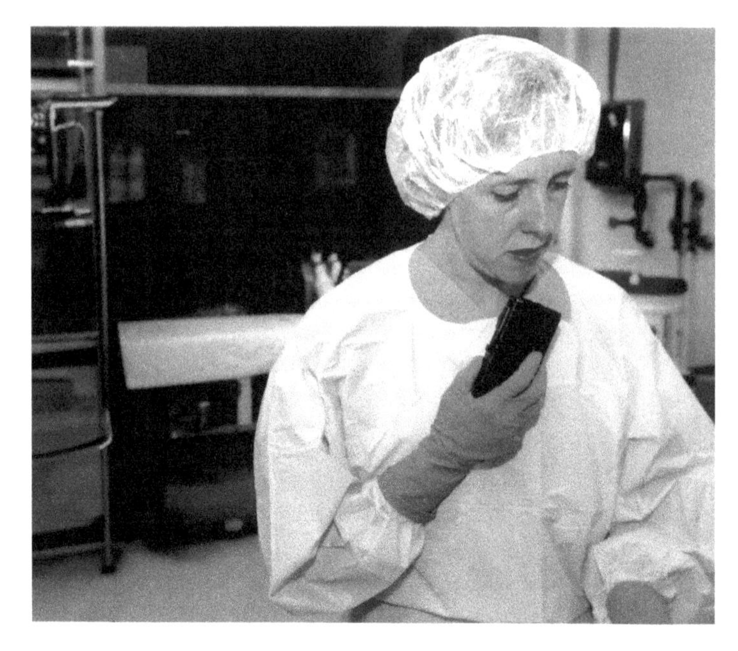

Author in West Onondaga Street Morgue, Syracuse, NY,
photo by Tim Reese, staff photographer, Syracuse Herald Journal, 1996

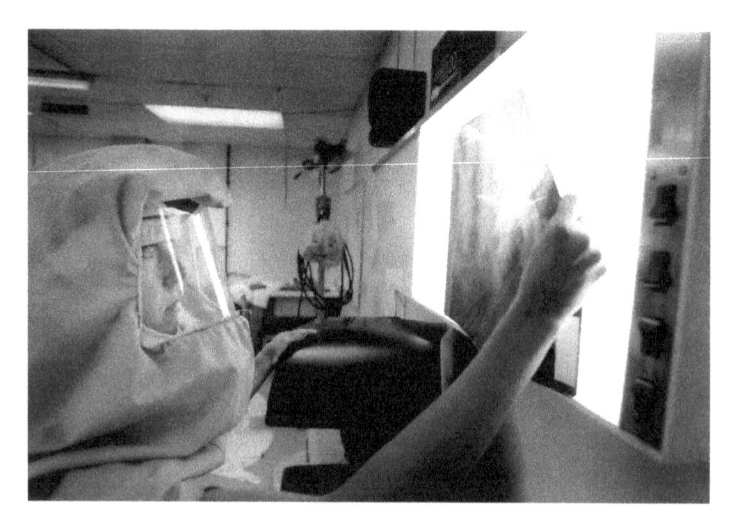

Author in West Onondaga Street Morgue, Syracuse, NY,
photo by Tim Reese, staff photographer, Syracuse Herald Journal, 1996

Author in office, Center for Forensic Sciences, Syracuse, NY circa 1999

Author's badge from deployment to World Trade Center Attacks, 2001

Author at home with family remembering 9-11, 2002

Author with US team for Thailand tsunami response, 2005, published in American Society for Clinical Pathology, 2005 and Medical Alumni Bulletin, University of Maryland, 2006

Family sending message to author in Thailand, 2005

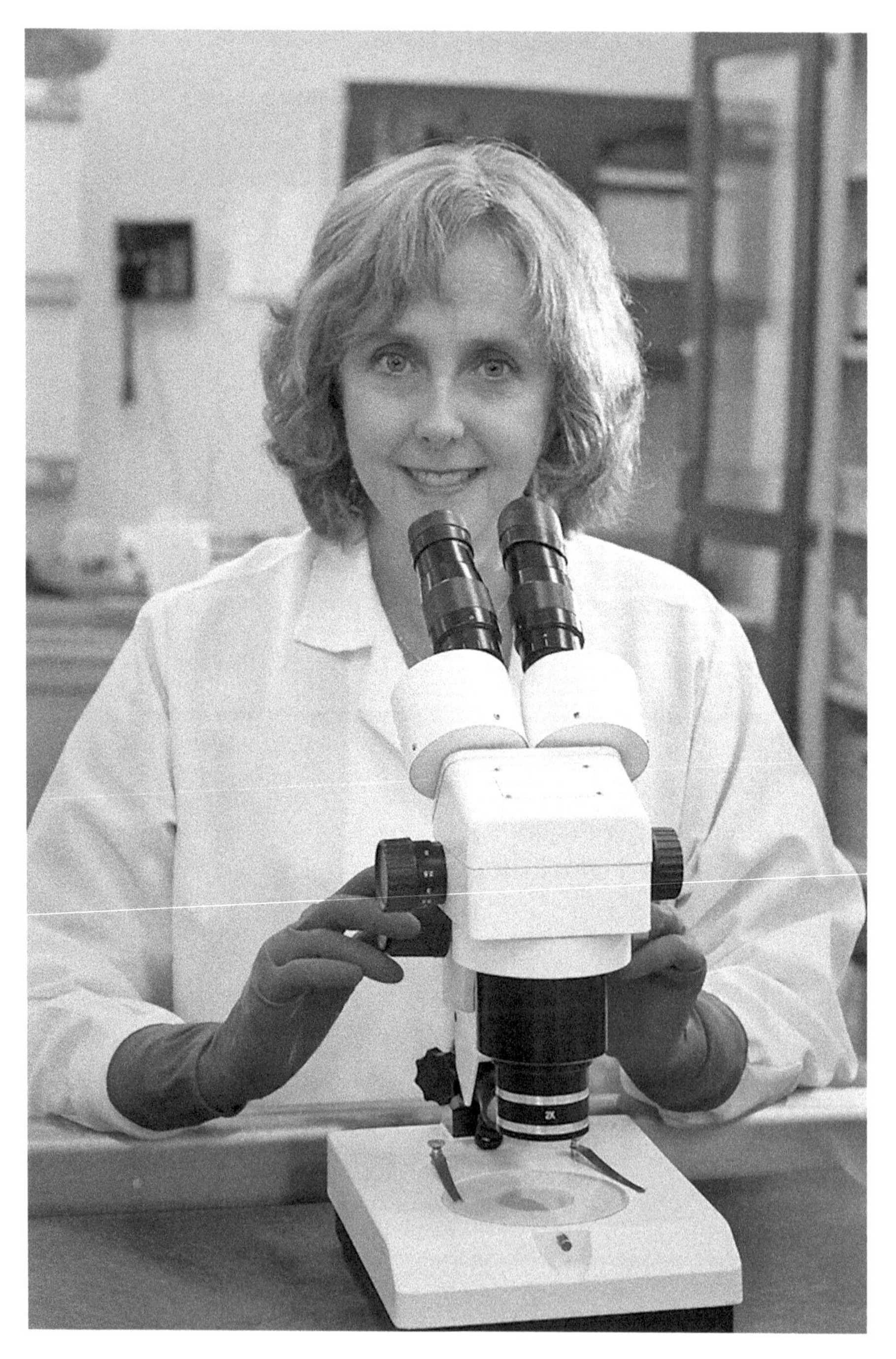

Author in Center for Forensic Sciences morgue, 2008

Author in Center for Forensic Sciences morgue, 2008

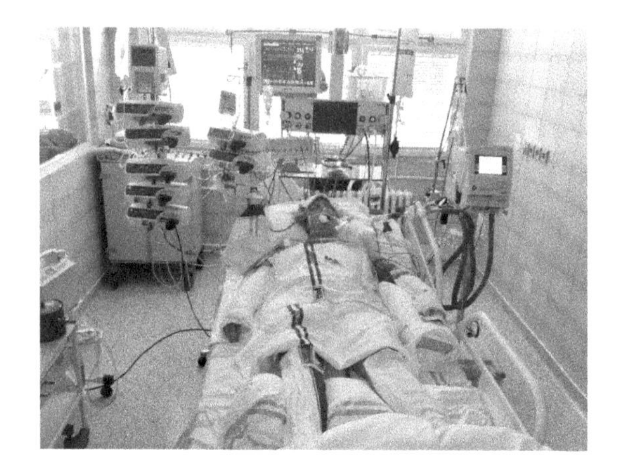

Author in Bulovka Hospital, Prague, 2012

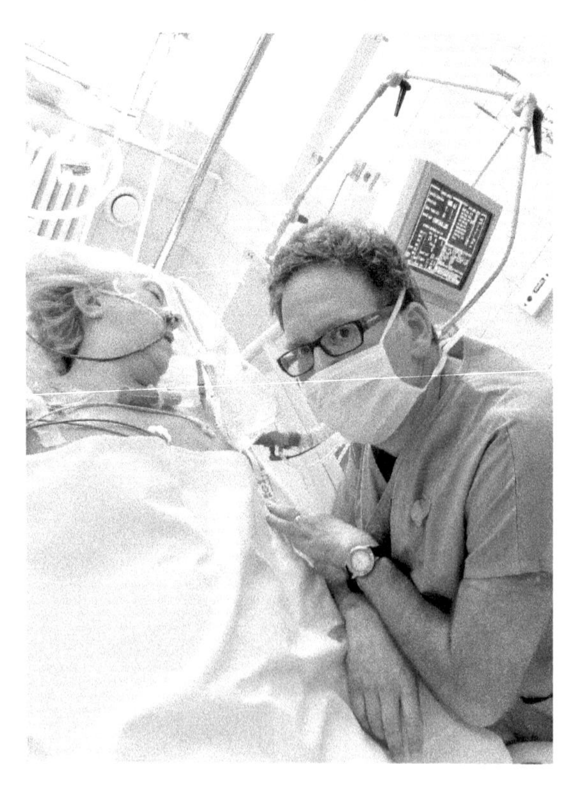

Author with husband, Bulovka Hospital, Prague, 2012

Author recuperating at home, 2012

Death as My Colleague

My mother was diagnosed with terminal metastatic pancreatic cancer two months prior to her demise. The moment her internist palpated her liver edge during an abdominal exam I knew the prognosis. The enlarged liver meant the disease had already spread.

We had gone to the doctor because my normally indefatigable mother felt tired. She had slowed down at home, slept more, and ate less. Before this, at 79 years of age, she exuded youthful energy, bustling around the house taking care of my three sons, playing with them in the yard, and walking the neighborhood daily. After she fired three different services that helped with the house cleaning, she informed me that I should pay her as she did a better job anyway. Fatigue was not in her vocabulary.

As we sat in that exam room, I saw the future of her rapid decline. I was a physician but a daughter too, so we went through a CT-guided biopsy that confirmed the hopelessness of widespread pancreatic cancer.

Standing in our living room, light streaming through the sky lights, I told my ever-optimistic mother the pathology results. She howled like a wounded animal and collapsed into my arms. I held her and stroked her head though I wanted to howl too. She grieved then but never again cried in sorrow.

We made the decision in tandem: no chemotherapy, radiation, surgery, or further diagnostic testing. My mother and I had previously planned a trip for her upcoming 80th birthday, a cruise to Alaska, just the two of us. I asked her if she wanted to go somewhere else sooner with me; I predicted she had less than two months left.

"I love you, honey, but I want to be with all my family—Marc, Joshie, Dave, and Marty," she said. Her grandsons were aged nine, seven, and two years. She was a third parent to them, living with us since the oldest was born. They had infused her retirement with purpose and joy.

We went on a family cruise—all six of us—savoring the time together. My mother accompanied us every evening to the elegant dining hall though she ate very little. We sunbathed on the deck while the kids went to ship camp. We played cards and joined in trivia contests. Sometimes in the evenings after dinner, we listened to live music, and she took a twirl on the dance floor with each of her grandsons.

One shore excursion led us to a nude beach. The boys played in the sand. Marc went to get drinks from the bar. I sat down on a blanket with Mom. After a few minutes she sat up very straight. She had noticed the naked people.

"Is this okay, Mom?" I said, realizing this might make her uncomfortable.

Her eyes scanned the beach and came to rest on one gentleman walking at the water's edge.

"I don't know what he has to strut about," she said.

I laughed, hard, giddy with this comment from a woman who I presumed had only seen one adult male naked, my father.

By the afternoon, she was playing the steel drum with the musicians, all of them clothed.

In private, I cried, afraid that each moment might be the last to share with Mom.

We returned from our trip on a Saturday. Mom and I drove to the grocery store to restock the family refrigerator. She pushed the cart, leaning on it for support. We lingered as we strolled up and down each familiar aisle, having done it hundreds of times before, and knowing this would be the concluding ritual.

At home, I tucked my tired mother into bed, where she slept peacefully. The next day, she awoke with a 104-degree fever, in and out of consciousness. I became the frightened daughter of a dying patient. Should

I call an ambulance or drive her to the hospital? Did she have a blockage or pneumonia that could be treated? Could I save her for a few days or weeks?

I spoke with Mom's doctor, and she explained (in that hopeful manner only oncologists can express) that this was a treatable episode. A surgeon could drain an obstructed bile duct. A hospitalist could treat Mom with intravenous antibiotics. The hospice representative was due to arrive the next day.

I hung up the phone. My mind seized up with the click of the disconnected telephone. I sat on the stair landing, my legs curled up to my chest. As a physician, I knew the bleak and painful consequences of sepsis, whatever its source. As a daughter, my mother was dying. I desperately wanted hope. Shakily I went to her room, the portable phone still cradled in my hands.

"Mom," I whispered as I brushed the damp hair off her forehead. She opened her glassy eyes, and a smile began at the corners of her dried lips.

"My princess," she murmured.

I explained our choices, unable to consider this weighty decision alone —the scared little girl, needing her to be my mommy.

"I want to stay here, Mary. Not die in the hospital with all those tubes and machines," she said with great effort.

I cried openly then and put my head on her chest. Her thin hand weakly gripped my shoulder. "I'll always be right here."

That painful night passed, alleviating my feeling that my decision would kill her quickly. Death's presence hovered in the house, waiting. My mother's body and spirit rallied—the fever broke. She telephoned friends.

After asking about their welfare, she said unhesitatingly, "I'm dying and just wanted to talk to you one last time."

Some sounded shocked and were unable to acknowledge this raw honesty. Others offered condolences, shared memories, and said farewell. Close friends came to visit and said good-bye in person.

One Friday morning, at the last minute, I kept the boys home from school. Mom instructed me to retrieve some packages from her closet, presents she bought at every opportunity and doled out to her grandsons throughout the year. Joshua, David, and Marty gathered around her bed as she gave them parting gifts: sticker books, action figures, dream catchers. They opened wrappings and oohed and aahed with each discovery. Paper and boxes littered the floor like at a birthday celebration. They spent the whole day with her. Joshua read her a story. David fed her pudding. Marty took a nap cuddled next to her. I felt restful that night.

The next morning, Marc and I prepared for her daily bath. We would carry her to the tub filled with warm sudsy water and sponge her down. It wasn't difficult for us; she weighed less than 90 pounds by then. Skin hung from her bony frame, bright yellow from the cancer that had consumed her liver. Her abdomen protruded, swollen and painful. The water would soothe her as we poured it over her chest and back and she sighed.

That day she did not want to get out of bed for her daily wash.

"Not today," she mumbled.

I tried turning her to change the damp sheets. She moaned in agony.

"Okay, Mom, okay," I replied as I rolled her slowly to her back. "I'm sorry."

Those two words carried more than an apology for the physical pain I caused her. I'm sorry you are dying. I'm sorry you won't get to see your grandsons become Bar Mitzvah. I'm sorry you'll never again go to the Knights of Columbus dances you loved so much or eat your nightly banana with Cheerios or play pinochle with me on a Saturday afternoon. I'm sorry I won't hear "little princess" anymore. I'm sorry your life is ending like this, that it must end at all.

Because we had chosen to avoid interventional therapy—hospitalization, treatment, and an invasive tube to drain toxic fluid from a blocked system that would inevitably clog again—there could be no feeding tubes or intravenous fluids. When she refused to eat solid food, we fed her small spoonfuls of strained squash or vanilla ice cream. Her intake was minimal. She did not have the stamina for more than a few mouthfuls. Then she stopped drinking, taking only sips of flavored water through a straw and, at the end, only allowing us to wet her lips.

The hardest part was her worsening pain despite hospice providing high dose medication. My heart broke anew when each turn of her body caused her agony.

The night of the day she refused a bath, one day after the fete with the boys, Marc woke me up as I fitfully slept. We had gotten into the rhythm of taking turns sleeping with my mother. We didn't want her to be alone at the final breath.

"Mary, I think Mom is going to die tonight," he quietly said. "She has the death rattle."

I gathered our sons and went to her room. I lay next to her, two boys on the other side of her, the third on a child's sofa on the floor, Marc next to him. Mom lay on her back, ashen colored even in her jaundiced luminescence, breathing erratically through cracked lips, encrusted secretions at the corners of her mouth and eyes, pain visible in facial grimaces.

I hugged her gently and the boys did too. They easily fell back to sleep. Despite knowing this was the end, I drifted off as well.

I awoke with a start. Something was wrong. I no longer heard her troubled breathing in my ear.

She was gone. I felt for a pulse that I knew wasn't there on skin still warm to the touch. I put my ear to her chest, my cheek to her lips and heard no heartbeat, felt no air movement. I pronounced her dead.

"Mom just died," I said.

Everyone had awakened with my rustling. We cried, even Marty joined. We took turns having a final visitation with her. Each of us, including the toddler, placed a single rose, her favorite flower, on her chest and spent a few minutes with her. The red blooms bought a few days earlier, contrasted with the pale nightgown and her yellow skin.

We said good-bye.

The next day I got a package in the mail, a vase with 24 synthetic red roses arranged with baby's breath and fern in a permanent bouquet. Esther had ordered them 10 days earlier. My mother loved roses and used every special occasion to visit the florist and buy a bouquet: all the boys' birthdays, Marc and my anniversary, friends visiting for the weekend, a good report from school. Marc had told her it was excessive. The silk flowers were beautiful. They seemed to say, "Here take these for all those times I would have bought you flowers." It was my mother's final gift.

Seventy-nine years of living, two months of dying. My family acknowledged Death and invited him into our home. He sat in a corner, patient and polite. We sat with him, Mom with a conspiratorial look from time to time. They had a mutual agreement—she said her farewells and prepared her only child for the hardest thing to face in life, and Death had waited.

Workday

It was "Take Your Daughter to Work Day," 1998. I had sons.

The Polaroid is slightly out of focus but shows the joy my two older boys had when visiting the old morgue on West Onondaga Street. They are dressed in white plastic gowns, bunched at the waist to avoid tripping on the lower edge, the adult size too large for them even though they were tall for their ages at seven and nine years old. Transparent face shields can't hide their playfulness. Blue surgical gloves cover their hands. Black belts at their waists hold up HEPA filters, the kind we used every day in the morgue. The excess of the belt hangs down almost to their feet from their tiny waists. Tubing from the filters peeks from behind the hoods on their heads. They look like miniature investigators for the CDC.

They stand in front of wooden doors that have reinforced metal along the mid portions which protected the wood from the daily traffic of gurneys but emitted bangs and clangs as the stainless steel of the portable tables made contact going in and out. Shelves can be seen holding supplies: sanitizer, gloves, disposable gowns. Leaning against the shelving is a "Caution, Wet Floor" sign, warning of the perennial hazard of slipping on a disinfected floor. An edge of the light box for viewing x-rays is seen at one side. The room looks more workshop than medical. The boys' outfits give it a scientific air.

Marty is absent from the picture. He was just two and a half years old at the time. He stayed at home with our nanny, Baba, who we hired after my mother died. Since Marc and I worked as full-time physicians, we needed care for our three sons.

The day Baba came to interview, she got down on the floor and started playing with Marty. She didn't speak English but communicated so much love with body language. Baba would continue to nurture Marc and me and the boys as well. We had Sunday dinners with her and her husband, Misha. Home cooked *pelmeni* (dumplings), borscht, and blinis became staples in our home. She became our adopted mother and grandmother. I learned Russian. We took vacations together blending our families.

I got the idea to have Joshua and David visit my office when the County announced support for the national event aimed at providing girls a glimpse into the working world of parents. Five years later the day would officially include boys.

After promising cleanliness and patient privacy, I got permission from the Health Commissioner. Anything related to an actual corpse was put away; all evidence sealed and locked up. We scrubbed all surfaces to a reflecting shine. The old building had never looked so good.

My kids were there to learn how I spent my days. I wanted to show them the science. In the autopsy room, my assistant, Glenn, helped the boys suit up into the personal protective equipment (PPE). He laid out the instruments. I explained how I used each one and took care of the decedents. At 26, Glenn was still boyish and charmed mine by showing them x-rays of hands and skulls.

Back at my office, I adjusted the eyepieces on the microscope.

"Can you see anything?" I said. Joshua was the first to try.

At my direction, he turned a knob to bring the histologic slide into focus. He bit his bottom lip in concentration.

"It's blue and pink," he said.

"Good. Each organ in the body has its own special cells. The heart is different from the liver."

"And the lungs are different, too, right?" David said. He remembered the human anatomy model I had shown everyone in his class.

I smiled. "Absolutely."

In the common workspace, another worker lifted each boy up so they could Xerox themselves. BATO had started out as an attendant at the age of 19 and worked his way up to forensic investigator. His real name was Brian, the same name as my husband's brother. To avoid confusion when he called my home, he clarified that he was "Brian at the office." Maybe because we worked in government, or simply because it amused us, he and I started using the acronym, BATO, as his nickname.

Those images of little boys' hands and faces squished against the copier remained pinned on my wall for years.

My secretary put a headset on each boy in turn so they could hear how I recorded descriptions of my cases.

"I type up the words that Dr. Jumbelic says and make it into a report," Gloria told them. "Oh, and I make sure she is on time for all of her appointments." She winked at them. She always made sure I was headed in the right direction.

"Is Mommy late sometimes?" David said.

"Yes," she said. "We call it Jumbelic time. Usually that means 15 minutes late."

Joshua and David laughed.

All three of my boys came to learn the names of my co-workers, interacting with them at the office and social gatherings. One of the doctors liked to take them to Disney movies so she wouldn't have to go alone. BATO, who had a great taste in clothes, gave them cool hand-me-downs as they grew up. They had a fondness for Glenn. He treated them as if he were a much older brother who didn't live at home anymore.

I had been working with Glenn ever since I arrived in Syracuse in 1995. He had started his career like BATO, as a morgue attendant, handling the receipt and release of bodies. Working hard, asking questions, and learning new skills, he was promoted to technician. His main duties involved assisting the pathologists during the autopsy procedure, and supervising equipment and supplies. He had the difficult task of getting the morgue ready in the morning and then cleaning it up at the end of the day. The job required mental acuity, physical strength, manual dexterity, and a good amount of tolerance for blood and guts and other slimy things.

For three years, we worked in that old building, originally an office space that was retrofitted to house a morgue. We wore bulky PPE, just like the kids tried on, for all autopsies. Overhead ultraviolet lights prevented infection with tuberculosis. The combination of the safety helmet, mask, and hissing ventilation made it impossible to converse.

Glenn and I developed a sophisticated system of non-verbal communication—gestures for stop and go, directions (up, down, right, left), and specialized signals for instruments. Extended index and middle fingers opening and closing meant scissors. A thumb and index finger pinching together indicated forceps. If I mimicked dabbing with my first three fingers, I wanted gauze. A pouring type of motion demonstrated that suction was needed. Glenn cut through the air for a knife and put hands together for a bowl.

Even after moving to the brand-new Center for Forensic Sciences building, we kept up our hand-gestured language. Occasionally, we leaned into each other to be heard and bumped our heads together. This dislodged the inner strap of the helmet, like that in a hard hat, necessitating a clean pair of gloves to refasten the apparatus.

Glenn mimicked the children's rhyme: "It's raining, it's pouring. The old man is snoring. He bumped his head and went to bed and didn't get up in the morning."

We laughed.

A white board hung on the wall where we recorded the weights of the internal organs. Sometimes, we left notes for each other. "Back in 10," Glenn wrote. "Meeting at 2," I penned. We had a radio/CD player on the side. Reception was sporadic so we mostly used the player. Whoever got to the morgue first, had their choice of music. Because of Jumbelic time, Glenn's choice of Blink 182 often played.

Mornings were frequently wordless in the autopsy suite, but afternoons brought sit-down chats in my office. One of us brought chocolate, mostly Reese's peanut butter cups. This began when at eight-months pregnant, I coveted his candy bar. Generously, Glenn shared it with me. Owing him one in return, we divided mine the next day. In less than a week, a tradition was born.

Glenn came to my office at 3 o'clock on the dot and plopped down in the visitor's chair. Either he had a confection with him, or I pulled open my desk drawer to expose my stash of sweets. We always rationed the one bar, each taking half.

Sometimes he talked about a movie he'd seen, or I'd tell him about the great dinner my husband made. Other times we were contemplative: I mused about the kids and their futures; he talked about professional aspirations. We shared our troubles, too.

On my first day back to work after my mother's funeral, we had a busy day in the morgue. At 3 p.m., Glenn tapped on the door while I was putting on my coat, planning to leave early.

"What's up?" I asked. In my sorrow, I'd forgotten our usual meeting.

In his hands he had a gift-wrapped package. He came in, closed the door, and put the object on my desk. Had I forgotten an important date: anniversary, birthday? Was this for someone at the office and he wanted to show me first? Glenn had been at the funeral, along with all my co-workers. What could this be?

Carefully, I removed the tissue paper to reveal a black frame with a cream-colored mat. In the center, a single dried red rose lay surrounded by sprigs of white baby's breath. At the right lower corner, was the word, Mom, written in calligraphy from gold cardboard with strips of crimson velveteen ribbon behind it. I recognized the decorations from the bouquet I had displayed at my mother's wake.

"It's beautiful," I said, "but how?"

"My dad did this for my grandma when she died. It was a wonderful way to remember her," Glenn said. "We have it up in the living room."

Glenn had gone to a lot of effort: collecting the flower, flattening it, cutting the ribbon and paper, gluing everything together, and framing it.

"Turn it over," he said.

"To Mary," it read. The use of my first name touched me. "Just one more of the several million things you have to remember your beautiful Mother by." How tender that he had personalized her by capitalizing mother. "You're a lot like her. That's why you're such a memorable person." This felt the highest form of compliment, a comparison to my adored mom. "Love Always, Glenn."

I hugged the frame, and then him.

"This means so much to me," I said.

That day we didn't have chocolate.

The remembrance still hangs in my home office next to a black and white portrait of my mother.

Glenn rose to the rank of Forensic Investigator and then on to become an Onondaga County Sheriff's Deputy, a childhood dream fulfilled. When he left the MEO, he gave me a card with a picture of him. It is an outdoor black and white portrait. Light dapples his face through an overhead bough of trees. He wears his hair short, his white tee-shirt crisp. His broad smile, big dimples, and wrinkles by his eyes, invite me to smile with him.

The card reads "Adios, Amoeba. You've been my boss and my friend. Now that I'm leaving, I guess you'll just be my FRIEND."

Glenn died in November 2003, in a tragic accident. As a Sheriff's Deputy, he had stopped to help a stranded motorist in a blizzard.

The night it happened, BATO called me.

Brrring. Brrring. Brrring.

The phone rang in the kitchen as my family, and I finished dinner.

I answered it. As I heard the information, I slid down the wall to the floor with the telephone receiver in my hand. Everyone quieted in the room, the only sound, my sobs. When Joshua, David, and Marty heard me say "Glenn," they cried. Marc hugged me and the five of us huddled together.

Glenn was my friend, and like a son to me. He taught me how to mother my little boys into young adults. He helped me build a bridge between them and their futures.

On Highway 481, a section is dedicated to him. A large brown sign with white letters reads "Deputy Sheriff Glenn Searles Memorial Bridge." It is a way for the community to remember.

I have the framed rose.

Collapse

DARK hair matted on the little girl's head. Her lips were dried and cracked and her eyes sunken. The olive tone of her skin paled. At less than fifth percentile for height and weight, Amina lay gaunt on the morgue table.

I sharpened my pencil, preparing to take notes. Feeling sluggish, I considered a cup of coffee, having not slept well the night before. Marty was the same age as this girl, four years old. In the wee hours, he had crawled into my bed and snuggled against me under the down blanket.

"Mommy?" he whispered. Taking my face in both his hands, he turned me to him. He felt as warm as a space heater. His cheeks were wet from crying.

"What's wrong, honey?" I said. The bedside clock read 2:02 a.m.

"I had a bad dream," he said, gulping breaths between words.

"Shh, it's not real," I said, wrapping my arms around him. We talked about thoughts and visions until we drifted off to sleep. The alarm woke us at 6 o'clock. For Marty, nightmares were monsters under the bed, made real by two older brothers telling R. L. Stine stories after dinner. For me, they were embodied in a child's corpse.

I skipped the coffee and did what I had promised Amina's family: a quick yet thorough examination. They were Muslim and it was customary to bury the dead as soon as possible. The autopsy took under an hour. With a child this small, the dissection was easy. Without disease, the tissues cooperated with me—every organ in its proper place, no scarring, no tumors, no bleeding, no trauma. The only abnormalities were an empty stomach and collapsed bowels from 24 hours of vomiting and diarrhea. Pencil thin intestines rested in the abdomen; their contents purged and without the usual odor of guts. My insides twitched in sympathetic response. The internal findings confirmed what I had seen on the outside of the body: severe dehydration.

Earlier that day, I met with Munir, the father, and extended family in their small two-bedroom apartment. Amina's mother, Nejra, sat on a worn sofa in the living room, head bent down, ready to collapse into herself, Munir by her side. Six other relatives were clustered on chairs hastily pulled into a semi-circle around the couch.

Munir told me, through an interpreter, about the rapid illness. Amina had gotten sick more than a day before, in the middle of the night. She threw up the homemade broth she'd had for dinner. Throughout the morning and afternoon, she had unrelenting liquid bowel movements. Then the fever started and even sips of water made her gag.

In the evening, the parents and sick child made their way to the nearest emergency room, a mile from their home, via the bus. The hospital was unfamiliar territory, as was the city. Amina's family was from the Balkans, recent refugees to Syracuse and part of the diaspora created by the civil war. There was no translator in the ER; no one understood what was going on with this little Bosniak girl. The nurse practitioner gave her an antibiotic for an ear infection and sent her home.

This family had survived ethnic cleansing; their village burned to the ground. They escaped famine and disease 4,000 miles away. Yet Amina died of an illness that modern medicine could cure. A simple intravenous line would have replaced the lost body fluids and essential salts. Without this salted liquid, the heart stopped.

"What did they do at the hospital?" I said. "Did they give her some saline into her veins? Check her blood pressure and pulse? Give her medicine to stop her vomiting?"

As the representative from the refugee center interpreted my words, Munir shook his head with each question. I confirmed his story later when reading every word of the one-page medical record.

Returning to their home from the hospital, Nejra took Amina into her arms and crooned to her. The child's fidgeting slowed. They fell asleep entwined. The mother was grateful that her daughter had stopped needing the bathroom.

In the morning, Amina's face felt cool, and Nejra thought the fever had broken. But there was no breath, no heart beating in the thin chest. Nejra wailed, a sound primeval that woke Munir and the entire house of aunts, uncles, and nephews.

After the autopsy, I did two things for Amina. I filed a complaint of negligence to the disciplinary board of the hospital and the state. Carefully turning her body, I pointed her head toward Mecca.

Feral Child

I never saw the little girl in the flesh, only in pictures.

The official call to 9-1-1 was logged in at 1:30 in the morning. Emergency responders did not attempt resuscitation; the six-year-old had clearly been dead for hours. Lying face-up in bed, dressed in a fresh one-piece pajama, her hair was wet. The bedding was gone—no sheets or pillow.

The parents gave vague, confusing, and conflicting accounts of the evening's events to the police's questions about when the girl had eaten or was last seen alive. In one version, two sisters, 8 and 4 years of age, who slept in the same room, had woken up to the little girl shrieking. Upset by this, they went to another room. The parents could not recall what time that had happened. The sisters were not interviewed.

The police found the body lying supine in the bottom bunk of a three-tiered set of beds. Her features suggested Indigenous ethnicity. Her right arm was bent 90 degrees at the elbow with her hand flat on her abdomen. Her other arm, bent at a more obtuse angle, had the fingers flexed as if grabbing something. Both hands were darkly discolored.

The father had customized this bunk bed for Berta, as he affectionately called her. He placed a mattress directly on the floor to create a bottom level below the usual two-tiers. He defined the margins with wooden two-by-fours. By screwing child safety gates into the fixture, barricades formed at the head and foot ends of the bunk. On a separate frame, he stretched plastic netting taut that ran the long axis and formed a hinged opening. He latched this enclosure from the outside, creating a cage, like a rabbit hutch. The mom referred to this pen as a fort, something she testified that "all the kids enjoyed, even fought over." Both parents claimed the contraption kept the little girl safe at night. None of the other children slept in animal crates.

The girl's sunken eyes with parted lids gave her a surprised look. Dried lips partially opened in a straight line. Bruises peeked out from beneath tousled hair on the forehead and cheeks. A pair of knotted red tights draped over her left arm; a brown cloth sash curled over her legs.

The parents admitted that they had used the tights and sash to restrain their daughter, but claimed the bindings were loose, and allowed her to turn and roll. They did this for Berta's own protection; they worried she would harm herself or one of her siblings. The mom said that a few days earlier, while giving Roberta a bath, the girl had scratched at her mother and pulled the mother's hair. No one examined the mom's skin to verify her story. The mom insisted the girl would get up at night and wander, once stealing a Pepsi from the kitchen.

The parents described blindfolding the girl to help her sleep through the night. They never admitted to the gag. They did not explain why her hair was wet.

With my professional experience in analyzing cases of child abuse and neglect, I was asked to consult as an expert witness in this little girl's death. In my Syracuse office, investigative records, photographs, and autopsy reports littered my desk. Dark data that, even after years spent separating my work and personal lives, silently followed me home.

As I ate dinner prepared by my husband, with the two older boys tussling for an extra chicken leg, her gaunt, malnourished figure stood in shadow. When I read *Stuart Little* to my youngest son, Marty, snuggled around me, Roberta's hollow eyes watched. During my morning routine, her visage reflected in the shower stall.

Roberta's tan skin blossomed with injuries. Bruises shone on her forehead, cheeks, and the sides of her neck along the blood vessels. Scrapes lined the inner lips matching contact with her own teeth where something had been forced against her mouth.

Marks on the wrists and ankles showed where Roberta had struggled against the cloth ligatures and rubbed her skin raw. The wounds were of differing ages, some fresh, others, days to weeks old. The little girl had been tied up repeatedly while she continued to fight her confinement.

Her skinny torso, prominent ribs and spine, wasting muscles, and lack of subcutaneous fat indicated severe malnutrition. Despite a kindergarten teacher praising the family for packing lunches of sandwiches with homemade bread, Roberta was starving.

The internal autopsy revealed extensive bleeding in the tissue of the scalp, with bruises the size of beer coasters where punches landed on her head. Spanking caused more hemorrhaging in the muscles of her buttocks. Chunks of vomit blocked the nostrils; a few stray specks landed on the adjacent skin. A last dinner of oatmeal filled up her trachea all the way to the lungs, leaving no room for air.

The coroner listed the cause of death as asphyxiation. The body was deprived of oxygen. Roberta spent her final moments unable to move, see, or speak, and choking on her own puke.

The parents had ready explanations for the wounds—Roberta inflicted them on herself. She was a headbanger and a self-harmer. No one except the parents ever saw this behavior.

Roberta was not an easy child. She came to the foster care system with an extensive medical and psychological history—Reactive Attachment Disorder, Post Traumatic Stress Disorder, and chronic sexual abuse. As a toddler, she suffered acts of cruelty committed by her drug-addicted biologic parents and their associates, including sodomy and rape.

This ordeal led to aberrant behavior. Roberta touched her genitalia in public and rubbed against objects as if pantomiming what had been done to her. She tried to initiate this same type of contact with males, both adults and children. Her sexual audacity bothered this devout community. The prior foster family had given Roberta up when the girl made up stories against the father and brother.

Social services considered Roberta unadoptable. After the failure in foster care, it seemed she might need placement in an institution for life. The little girl also had depression.

Despite the girl's bleak history, the Evers family petitioned Social Services to take Roberta in. At first, the agency refused, citing her difficult behavior, but the parents persisted. Formal adoption proceedings noted the "family is among the highest caliber of families providing foster care in the southwestern region of Colorado."

This mother and father raised seven biological children, adopted four others, and fostered 60. Neighbors described the parents as loving and compassionate, respected, and well-liked.

"For we are God's handiwork, created in Christ Jesus to do good works, which God prepared in advance for us to do." Ephesians, 2:10. To the community, the family exemplified this doctrine.

Roberta joined the Evers family 18 months prior to her death.

The holiday photo that year shows the father sitting on a loveseat next to his wife. Three youngsters, two boys and a girl pile onto their parents' laps. A semi-circle of eight more siblings gathers around. Everyone is smiling. They are dressed in white shirts, vests, ties, black dresses, and frilly collars. Roberta, perched on the man's left knee, is laughing.

Dark hair frames the little girl's face, bangs brushed unevenly to the sides. Her mouth is opened wide with exuberance. She seemed excited for Christmas.

At the trial, the parents made no mention of this occasion. They portrayed Berta as a youth with a wild streak who defied rules; she ignored basic instructions regarding eating and sleeping. The mother and father claimed the girl smashed her head into furniture and walls and vomited for attention. They even said she molested others. Roberta was six years old.

They spoke of her nature as primitive with no concern for consequence. Berta had dramatic mood swings. Though potty-trained, she urinated and defecated on herself. They resorted to putting her in diapers, thermal underwear, and one-piece sleepers. The multiple layers contained her soiling and kept her from exposing and touching herself. At night, the parents found her wandering through the house, so they devised a safeguard by tying her up in a special bed.

"We were only trying to salvage a little girl that other people had damaged," the father said.

The parents saw Roberta as incapable of normal socialization, a feral child. The dad explained her passing "was God's will." The police, medical examiner, and I disagreed with him.

Nearly a year after she was killed, I traveled to Durango, Colorado, to testify. The trip took 12 hours, three flights, and two layovers. The last leg of the 2,000-mile journey passed over the Southern Rockies. The mountains, retaining snow cover even in May, blended with the clouds. The jagged edges of the San Juan range emerged from the mist seemingly right below me. An ethereal vista contrasted with my corporeal thoughts.

Main Street traveled straight through town with two-story buildings along the sides. I surveyed the pickup trucks parked at the curbs. Horses would have suited the ambiance better. The Strater Hotel, built in the heyday of gold mining, opened onto a corner. Brick facade belied its history; wood columns and a second-floor balcony bestowed authenticity. Inside, a plaster-paneled ceiling, light sconces, and thick drapes supplied atmosphere. The reception fronted a wooden cubby with 39 skeleton keys, one for each guest room. This was the western frontier: the Four Corners region of the Southwest, where Utah, Arizona, Colorado, and New Mexico kiss. I had a sudden taste for whiskey.

I wandered to the bar. I ordered a boilermaker and listened to the player piano. Any minute, Butch Cassidy and the Sundance Kid might burst through a saloon door. I hovered between worlds of yesterday and today, metropolitan and borderland, nightmare and vision.

I spent the evening reviewing the reports before turning in for the night. Sleep eluded me despite exhaustion and soft bed linens. A reel-to-reel forensic film of Roberta looped inside my head.

The hotel offered a hearty breakfast for which I had no appetite. The mirror reflected my gray suit, business flats, and make-up camouflaging my tiredness. Black coffee fortified me as I walked the short distance to the courthouse.

A large crowd waited in front of the building. The trial garnered a lot of media attention; there were reporters from the *Rocky Mountain News* and the *Durango Herald.* Electa Draper, a staff writer for the *Denver Post*, covered it daily. The trial lasted 12 days.

Inside, Roberta's adoptive parents were seated at the defense table, looking their forty-something years, and soft around the middle. The mother was dressed in a dark tunic with a large white collar, Puritan style. The father had on an athletic jacket, casual enough for a sporting event. They both wore large-rimmed glasses, and somber faces. The mom frowned as I approached the witness stand; the dad stared at me.

Familiar as Roberta's face was to me, theirs were not, only viewed on a small polaroid. They didn't look like killers. Bland in demeanor, quiet in composure, they appeared ordinary. No one to whom I would give a second glance.

As Oscar Wilde said, "I have never met any really wicked person before . . . I am so afraid he will look just like everyone else." I felt a slight chill.

The bailiff swore me in on the Bible. I sat in the witness chair with a folder of records in my lap. The prosecuting attorney questioned me about the wounds. My words rendered the injuries into sizes and shapes, colors and textures. I detailed the events: battery, captivity, and starvation. I felt earnest in my testimony, looking at each juror as I answered.

When it was time for cross-examination, the defense lawyer barked questions:

"The girl did this to herself with her temper tantrums, right?"

"Couldn't she have accidentally hit her head on the bunk bed?"

"It's possible she banged her face deliberately on the bed frame, yes?"

"She threw up on purpose for attention, didn't she?"

All his queries received a definitive negative response from me.

He kept rephrasing and recasting, trying to wear away the answers, to find a gap to get purchase, hoping for a response he needed. Would any doubt he raised be reasonable?

The stuffy courtroom, packed like a city bus whose windows won't open, caused jurors to shift in their seats, wanting a coffee or smoke break. Objections shouted from the prosecutor interrupted my testimony and caused the judge to act as referee, sometimes allowing my answer, other times prohibiting it. Eventually, we came full circle to the defense's most important question.

"Didn't the child cause her own injuries?" he said.

I looked at the parents, sitting at the defense table, hands in their laps, heads bowed. A tired middle-aged couple caught up in the legal system; no hint of the brutal rage against Roberta. I stared at the back wall of the courtroom serving as a screen for my mind with the plethora of the little girl's injuries on display—punches to her head, slaps to her bottom, her arms and legs tied up in the form of a medieval rack, something forced against her mouth so hard that the vomit had nowhere to escape. I could almost smell the puke that she choked on in her cage. The fresh pajamas and shampooed hair made me wonder what other horrors had been washed away.

I longed to quote Lemony Snicket from his *Series of Unfortunate Events*, familiar to me from reading them to my three sons—"There are some circumstances so utterly wretched that I cannot describe them in sentences or paragraphs or even a whole series of books."

I only had one word for the attorney. "No."

The defense lawyer looked at his yellow legal pad and flipped through the pages. Someone coughed. A door opened and closed. The prosecutor leaned over to whisper to her assistant. A chair squeaked.

"No further questions, your Honor," he said.

The judge nodded to me and said, "You may step down."

My pulse hammered in my ears as I walked through the gallery, past the crowd of family supporters and scribbling journalists. I returned to the hotel feeling the impending disappointment of the future verdict.

Opening my briefcase, I placed the sealed manila envelope containing the scene and autopsy photographs, and the investigative and autopsy results, inside.

Even though the gruesome details of the crime were described in court, support for the parents ran high with 347 people signing a petition requesting the judge not to impose any jail time. The small town experienced cognitive dissonance. The horrible events occurred; the family was good.

An adult daughter pleaded, “Please don’t take them away from us. If we lost them, I don’t know what we’d do. They are our rock, our friends, and our parents.” She spoke for all the older children.

Police, social workers, and physicians had provided extensive testimony depicting a shocking life and end. The defense team spun a tale of a head-banging, bulimic, and somnambulant child, which therapists, child protective workers, and even the former foster mother disputed.

Colorado statute allows the use of physical force by a parent disciplining a child when “it is reasonably necessary and appropriate to maintain discipline or promote welfare.” It was hard to comprehend how any of the parents’ actions were reasonable, necessary, or appropriate.

Ultimately, the jurors found the parents responsible for Roberta’s injury but not her death. Instead, mother and father were convicted of the lesser charge of criminally negligent child abuse resulting in serious bodily harm. In legal terms, they hadn’t knowingly and recklessly caused her to die. The dad also received a felony conviction for tampering with evidence. The prosecution had proven that he cleaned up and altered the scene—the sheets, the ligatures, the body.

In an unusual move, following the verdict, the jurors wrote a letter to the judge.

They noted “a six-year-old girl was tied up and caged as a means of control and punishment, which led directly to her death . . . The seriousness of this crime should not be underestimated, nor should the danger to the community be minimized." Did their epistolary comments assuage their conscience?

The judge announced, "You left Roberta, not yet seven years old, contained in a bunk bed by barriers she could not leave, her hands and feet tied. She was restrained and alone. She was isolated, vulnerable, and helpless. It's beyond my comprehension that anyone could find such restraints acceptable. You abandoned her that night."

His moral speech did not affect the sentence he imposed. The magistrate had the power to levy up to six years in jail to the parents, but he reduced the term to six months for the father and three months for the mother. Their prison time was to be staggered so that one parent could be at home with the remaining children. The parents maintained permanent custody of all their biological and adopted kids but lost guardianship of their two current foster children.

The trial, the publicity, and the conclusion divided the small community. Many people were incensed that the mother and father had to spend any time in jail. Others couldn't believe the sentence was so short. One reporter noted that the family had been "alternately cast…as more wholesome than the Brady Bunch and creepier than the Addams Family." This dichotomy bewildered people. Somewhere between Roberta's murder and the legal drama, forensic science failed.

One question that perplexed townspeople was how this wholesome family that raised 10 normal children, and helped scores of others, could be so cruel to one child.

Experts testified this was classic target-child selection, where Berta was singled out for abuse because she was a difficult-to-manage kid, with problem behavior and a defiant attitude. The jurors opined in their letter, "A child died because she didn't fit an artificial image of perfection created by the family."

The father explained, "Roberta was just one of these kind of kids [*sic*] …No one understands how a child can destroy a family. This is a nightmare."

Yet the parents never requested assistance to deal with their mounting frustration. They never told Social Services about difficulties managing Roberta while she was alive. Witnesses confirmed that the little girl was often punished for bad behavior and spent a lot of time by herself, though they were ignorant of the methods used to control her. One social worker described Roberta as "a sad little girl" who was in her room three out of the four times he visited the home on routine checks. He never went into the chamber.

One sibling told a teacher in explanation for why Roberta was absent from school yet again. "She's always in trouble."

This family lived in a world modeled on Christian self-sufficiency.

"Whoever spares the rod hates their children, but the one who loves their children is careful to discipline them." Proverbs, 13:24. They loved their children; they made them obey.

At his sentencing, the dad asked the court "for forgiveness for our poor judgment. I am her father and take full responsibility." He said he "would feel pain, guilt, self-doubt, remorse and embarrassment as a convicted felon for the rest of my life." The longest part of his quote referenced his humiliation.

While in jail, the father read Foster Cline's 1997 *Discipline with Love and Logic*. The psychiatrist author promoted primitive attachment therapy, harsh holding methods of controlling wild children. One technique he popularized was re-birth simulation, swaddling a child completely in blankets and pillows. Cline eventually stopped this practice after a 10-year-old girl choked on vomit while undergoing the smothering procedure in a clinic.

"Had I met Cline before the trial, I probably wouldn't have gone to jail," the father stated in an interview in the publication *Westword* barely a year after the trial.

The psychiatrist had alleviated whatever guilt or remorse remained for the dad. The parents appealed the original ruling despite having already served their sentences. The court upheld the verdict.

The morning after my testimony, I awoke well before dawn. The trial was still underway; the verdict and sentencing loomed in the future. My flight back to New York was hours away. It was still too early to call home. Unsettled and restless, I packed my bags and made my way to the lobby. I felt an overwhelming urge to get out of town.

The overnight attendant looked up from his book.

"Is there anywhere I can rent a car at this hour?" I asked.

He stood up, smiling politely as if my request at 4:30 a.m. were routine.

"Unlimited miles?" he said.

I shrugged. I had no destination, just desire.

He handed me a pamphlet for Mesa Verde National Park, only a 30-minute drive. The tourist brochure promised an unforgettable view of the sunrise.

"Great idea," I said. He telephoned the car rental agency.

My packed suitcase sat in the trunk along with my briefcase of reports. Darkness surrounded me along Route 160, almost a straight shot west from Durango. Through the speakers, Natalie Grant sang her hit "There is a God," sweet and rhythmic. I wanted to believe her lyrics, that somewhere out there was a master plan.

Near Hesperus, I turned the radio off. The fragrance of wisteria drifted in through the open window. The National Park entrance wasn't open yet, but a nearby road took me to a vista of the 700-year-old Pueblo/Anasazi ruins. Cold air blew from the high plateau as I got out of the car and leaned against the hood, zipping up my jacket.

The sun's rays began to light the crevices of the ancient dwellings. Yellow and red hues played across windows and doorways. As the sun rose higher, a profusion of green came into focus, surprising in this desert environment without many verdant plants. The name of this place suddenly made sense—Mesa Verde, 'green table' in Spanish.

Details of the archaeological site emerged. Residences, made of sandstone, mortar, and wood beams, were built into rock overhangs. Homes clustered together forming stacked boxes with occasional towers for fortification. I wasn't sure which of the famous excavated buildings was in front of me. Consulting the diagram in the booklet, I decided it was Cliff Palace, the largest group of tightly packed apartments. About 125 people had lived in just that one edifice.

Until the end of the thirteenth century, nearly 20,000 Pueblos inhabited the region. A scarcity of water and increasing cold weather were one theory to explain their migration south, escaping the harshness and deprivation of a changing landscape.

I stared at the square and rectangular openings and thought of Roberta's bunk bed, her personal mesa, a bleak and harmful environment. Unlike the Anasazi, who trekked to Hopi and Navajo regions, this child had nowhere else to go.

The sun fully illuminated the dwellings and warmed my skin. The only sound was my breathing. A small breeze blew across the bangs on my forehead. I closed my eyes.

I whispered, over and over, "Roberta." My word rose skyward, a musical ostinato. Chanting louder, the melancholic leitmotif blurred her name to sobs.

An unconscious desire propelled me to this park, before opening hours, awaiting the dawn. Roberta's Chindi, the Navajo spirit left behind after death, lived in my mind. It was time to let her go.

A famous Navajo proverb states, "You cannot see the future with tears in your eyes."

I breathed deeply and then exhaled until my jaw hurt, attempting to expel her to the universe.

On the Way to School

I stood garbed in a white plastic coverall, hair bonnet, N-95 mask, and splash shield. My purple Crocs, dedicated morgue shoes, peaked out beneath my maroon scrubs. The PPE was standard but felt overdone for doing an autopsy on a six-year-old child.

The boy had been the front seat passenger in a car driven by his mother. They were on the way to school, just the two of them. Another car rear-ended them at a stoplight. Had the mom paused too long at a green light? Had she stopped suddenly on an amber? Was the other driver distracted or had the sun just caught his eye? I would have to wait for the police report. In the meantime, I reviewed the ambulance record.

The mother's neck had whiplashed from her head jerking forward and back during the collision. After the shock of the impact, she turned to her son and saw his head slumped forward. She screamed loudly.

An EMT was right on the scene. While getting a coffee at the corner bodega, he heard the familiar squeal and crunch of cars. Already heading toward the scene, the woman's cry made him hurry faster. He saw the boy in the passenger seat, face blue and respirations wheezy. Chest muscles pulled tight to the rib cage as the child tried to inhale. Pressing fingers at the neck, the medic felt for the pulse of the carotid artery, weak and slowing. As he undid the seatbelt and slid the child out of the car, he noted that the airbags had not deployed. The rescue team arrived quickly and transported the boy to the hospital with advanced life support continuing. That had been hours ago.

The mother sat sedated with a cervical collar in place in the Family Room of the Center for Forensic Sciences, a dimly lit space with soft-cushioned couches. She insisted on this quiet vigil that would end only when the autopsy was completed. She refused to go home until she knew what had happened to her son. BATO agreed to sit with her; he had a calm demeanor and caring patience. A small rack on an end table contained brochures about the stages of grieving with contact numbers for groups offering help with the process. It was too soon for this woman.

She waited for an answer from me. I was in the morgue.

The boy looked tiny on the autopsy table, vulnerable in his size and nakedness. I thought of my three sons. Images of them in the bathtub splashing and laughing contrasted with his still and silent form.

A thin line of blood oozed from the start of the Y-incision, like the first stroke of an artist's brush on a blank canvas. As the scalpel penetrated deeper, yellow globules of fat extruded, normally hidden beneath the white dermis of the skin. It took less than a minute to remove the bones of the front of the chest as the knife slid smoothly through the pliable cartilage next to the sternum.

I methodically examined each internal organ: the heart, lungs, liver, spleen, and kidneys. Working through from most to least likely injured, the dissection started with the aorta. When a body's forward motion is abruptly stopped in a crash, this large vessel can rip right off the heart. There is rapid exsanguination when the tear is complete. At times some gauzy layers remain with a final break occurring later. The person can be conscious initially only to suffer collapse on the way to the hospital. Ribs can fracture, which leads to outside air rushing in and collapsing the lungs. The remaining hard organs of the abdomen can lacerate and bleed.

None of these injuries appeared in this little boy.

His insides were a textbook lesson in normal anatomy. The lungs glistened pink without the ubiquitous black dots of urban living or smoking. The heart and viscera gleamed without years of unhealthy eating coating their surfaces. No wounds, broken bones, or blood poured into spaces where it shouldn't be.

My hands palpated the inner lining of the body and the spine, feeling for minuscule trauma. X-rays hung on the lightbox next to the autopsy table. I scrutinized them once more and still found no abnormality.

The stomach lay on my dissecting board. Both of its ends were clamped. I opened one and poured the contents into a measuring cup. Peach-colored fluid with chunks of scrambled eggs spilled out, a total of 10 ounces. The distinct aroma of orange juice wafted up. A pang of guilt hit me that I didn't make my boys breakfast that morning. They had waited for the school bus with their pop-tarts wrapped in paper towels. Maybe I would pick them up early and make them a special dinner.

I withdrew body fluids for toxicology—blood, bile, and urine, more than 300 mL and clear. The boy hadn't had a chance to go to the bathroom before rushing to the car.

I watched closely as my assistant removed the top of the cranium with great skill to avoid damaging the brain. There was a soft sound like opening a vacuum-sealed plastic bag. In car crashes, a common fatal injury is in the head. The forces generated cause the thin lining of the brain to tear. A multiplicity of blood vessels spidering through this tissue can rupture. The skull is a confined space so when the blood accumulates, pressure pushes on the brain which goes toward the spinal cord and damages the area that controls the heart and breathing. Circulation and respiration cease.

The outside of the head had no trauma. The inside of the skull was pristine. The tan curves of the brain reminded me of a coral reef. Everything inside looked normal.

The neck block was the only thing left for me to examine. Slicing along the edge of the tongue, I checked this red-brown muscle for small bruises. These show up when someone has a seizure and bites down hard. There were none. I opened the tubes of the throat starting with the esophagus; the pearly white lining appeared perfect. Anxiety rose inside me. Maybe there would be no answer for the weeping woman down the hall.

The airway was the very last structure, covered by a little flap of cartilage called the epiglottis. This valve coordinates breathing and swallowing. When it's working properly, eating and talking occur without conscious awareness of two side-by-side pipes. When it's not, a stray food particle enters the larynx resulting in hacking coughs. Below the epiglottis are the vocal cords, membranes moving like bellows to create speech. If something larger is inhaled instead of swallowed, talk ceases and the Heimlich maneuver is needed.

In the upper trachea, I found the problem. A glob wedged there, the size of a grape. It peeled easily away from the mucosa. The magnifying glass revealed ridges on its surface, indentations from teeth. I leaned closer. The odor of bubblegum rose to meet me.

I had the answer—intense in its simplicity.

"Can you photograph this?" I asked my assistant.

He stopped sewing the child's scalp closed and looked at the wad of pink chewing gum on the blue photo board. For a long moment, I stared with him.

"I'm going to talk to the mother," I said. I had uncovered the mystery of why she sat alive less than 50 feet away and her son lay dead within my reach. The words—your son choked on a piece of gum—sounded ludicrous.

I imagined the events. His mom hurriedly organized the car with a lunchbox, coffee, and a list of daily chores—a morning like dozens of others, a morning like many of mine. Her son sat quietly enjoying a Big-League Chew or Bubblegum cigar, a treat before school. Perhaps it had been from a gift bag at a friend's weekend birthday party. Maybe the boy had found it in a crevice in the seat or glove compartment. Ten minutes later, the jolt of the accident caused the gum to go down the wrong pipe and block his airway.

"Every mind must make its choice between truth and repose. It cannot have both," wrote Ralph Waldo Emerson. It was my duty to deliver the truth.

I removed my autopsy garb and headed to the Family Room.

Arson Bombing

"It was arson," Joshua said. At 11, his vocabulary reflected the forensic terms he heard during family discussions. He sat cross-legged on the floor amid a small group of kids.

"You don't know that," the teacher said.

"I do."

She paused in her recitation of the signs and symptoms people feel after a crisis. Temple Beth El had been firebombed. Though it wasn't our family's synagogue, its second floor housed the Montessori school that our three sons attended. Everyone had been dislocated and temporarily housed in a church, trying to maintain a normal schedule of classes.

The kids shifted restlessly.

"The fire was an accident," the teacher said.

The philosophy of nurturing a child's desire for knowledge touted by Maria Montessori seemed momentarily forgotten.

"But it really was arson. My mom told me. She's the ME. She knows the guys from the FBI and ATF," Joshua said.

Some of the children looked wide-eyed at him. One girl laughed. The string of letters must have sounded like a foreign language to his classmates. This was the year 2000, the first episode of CSI had just aired on television; the peak popularity of crime dramas and all the coded words that came with them was years in the future.

Later that day, my family sat at the kitchen table, plates full of spaghetti with a side of broccoli. I reached for a slice of bread. Marty pushed a meatball around his plate. At four, he didn't really like beef.

"Mom, was I right?" Joshua said after recounting the interaction.

"Yeah, I heard the same thing in my class," David said. He was in the six-to-nine-year-old age group. "But was the fire started by someone who hates Jews?"

The weight of the words made it difficult to eat.

The incident had occurred in October on the beautiful Jewish holiday of Sukkot, the celebration of surviving 40 years in the desert, and this year falling on the holy Sabbath, Friday night. Flames destroyed the entryway at the back of the synagogue and damaged the entire second floor with smoke. The building had been empty; no one hurt.

What if congregants or students had been there? Would they have been trapped inside by the flames? Would kids have huddled under desks breathing in the toxic fumes? What if the fire had destroyed the sanctuary? Would the *Bima* (holy altar) have burned or the beautiful Torah scrolls representing 4000 years of history gone up in the conflagration?

During my first visit to a synagogue, 16 years earlier, I was prepared to be underwhelmed. I came from a Roman Catholic tradition filled with icons and incense, pomp and circumstance. Yet despite the beauty of ceremony, after attending Catholic school until I was 18, I divorced myself from its traditions and tenets. In my young adult life, I floated without a spiritual anchor.

On that first connection with Judaism, I walked into a Reformed *Schul* (synagogue), just outside Baltimore, on *Shabbat*. My goal was to understand my boyfriend, Marc, who was wedded to his tradition as much as I was distanced from mine. What power did this tribe hold over him?

The inside of the building felt familiar but more subdued than a cathedral. The pews mirrored those in a church minus the kneelers. The centerpiece, usually a crucifix in Christianity, was an arc, a fancy closet behind the altar. Everyone stood chanting in Hebrew. Some people rocked back and forth as they prayed. The words crescendoed as the doors to the arc opened.

The rabbi and cantor removed the holy scrolls, holding them aloft by the handles; the paper and words too holy to be touched by human hands. They walked through the congregation and people extended their prayer books to the Torahs and then brought the books to their lips for an indirect kiss.

Tears gathered in my eyes. My skin felt warm. This adoration was for the written word. The seismic force of this realization overtook me. I formed a connection to the people gathered here celebrating the power of a book; brethren united for thousands of years through dedication to learning. I had found my spiritual home.

The arson in our town, an anti-Semitic act, felt directed at me and my Jewish family. David's question 'Was the fire started by someone who hates Jews?' still hung in the air.

"Someone deliberately set the fire," Marc said.

"Look," I said and reached out to either side of me to hold Marty's and David's hands. "The school does not want to believe that someone did this on purpose. But they're also scared so they don't want to rent space in another synagogue. It's complicated."

"Why, Mom?" the three boys said at the same time.

If the school thought this wasn't a targeted attack, why were people afraid of being in a temple? If the fire was an accident, then it might happen anywhere, anytime. If, however, it was a hate crime, people might be afraid to be in another Jewish building.

"Not everyone is as brave as King Christian," I said.

This story widely told in Hebrew school described how during World War II the King of Denmark asked his citizens, mostly Christian, to wear the star of David so that Jews wouldn't be singled out by the Nazis. Though maybe it was a myth, history showed that the Jews of Denmark were spared from many atrocities because of the support of their neighbors.

"Or strong like the people in the *Christmas Menorah*," I said, referencing a true story about Billings, Montana, from a few years earlier. The Jews in the town were being threatened and bombarded with hate mail, cemetery desecration, vandalism, and bomb threats due to an increase in neo-Nazi groups. When the winter holidays approached, the townspeople encouraged by the police chief and religious groups, all placed images of Menorahs, the holy candelabra of Hanukkah, in their windows to show their solidarity with the Jews of their city.

"Not everyone has courage," Marc said.

"Baba and Misha do," David said. The nanny and her husband had become our adopted grandparents, Jewish refugees from Russia emigrating when Gorbachev opened the doors nearly a decade earlier. We had heard their tales of struggle, an inability to practice religion, and fear of persecution.

"Yes, they are very brave," I said. Had this arson kindled fear for them, too?

"Is the school afraid of us?" Joshua said.

I wanted to shout—yes, yes, they are.

Before dinner, I had had a conversation with the director of the school. We talked about buildings available to relocate to and which ones were under consideration. I knew that all the rabbis in town had offered space. The director said some parents and teachers didn't want to be in a synagogue again. I emphasized we would be stronger together.

I became strident, my emotion leaking through the telephone line. If the school was uncomfortable operating out of a temple, then maybe people would be uncomfortable next to my Jewish children. I said as much. She told me not to come to the parents and teachers' meeting scheduled that evening; it would be unproductive.

"I spoke with the director. She said people are afraid of synagogues now." I held the sting of the talk with the director inside me.

The boys remained quiet.

I got up and began to clear the plates.

THE BACKPACK

THE backpack had been buried for seven years. Interred under layers of soil against a thick root of a maple tree, daffodils flowering above, it might have remained there, time slowly eroding the polyester fibers. But that's not how it happened. The father confessed. The rucksack contained his disintegrating newborn son.

The parents had been young teenagers at the time of the birth; the mother, 13 years old, the father a year older. What would I have done at that age? My only knowledge of sex had been gleaned from the Daughters of Chastity (my term). If a boy touched or kissed you, then a baby grew inside. It sounded confusing, messy, and full of germs. At 13, I still preferred to play with my Barbie doll creating adventures as a stewardess, her little blue Pan Am bag promising world travel.

In 2001, at 45, I sleuthed the cause of death from each body I examined. On rare occasions I disinterred clandestine graves. That's how I got involved with the search for the knapsack.

The call to find the infant had come into my office on a spring afternoon. A young man had informed the police that he knew where a homicide victim was hidden. Prior experience taught me that most of the time these tips on past crimes yielded nothing.

Once, an inmate had claimed that he knew where a murder had happened five years earlier. He led me to the exact location of the disposal of the corpse, specifying a gully with remarkable acuity. I supervised the operation. His story resulted in weeks of digging in the mud and an aching back. In the end, the prisoner had gone back to jail having enjoyed some time in the sun. No body was ever recovered.

After the telephone call from the police about the backpack, I responded to the site of the possible burial. The lead detective, Tom, and I stood on the back porch of a suburban home. A green expanse of lawn stretched about a quarter-acre to a deciduous tree line. Boxwoods and ferns hugged the deck with yellow bulbs lining the perimeter of the yard.

"This feels impossible," I said, referring to finding the tiny human submerged in this bucolic vista.

"I don't know, Doc," Tom said. "The boy told me where he put the baby. Sounded pretty sure." He nodded toward the forest. "Over there at 10 o'clock near that big maple."

I stared at the row of identical trees.

"He may feel confident, but it's been a long time and besides, this is a large tract of land. If he's off by one tree, it could take days, no, make that weeks to search."

Tom looked at the woods, 50 feet away. He pushed his hands deeper into his pockets.

"Why now?" I said. "I mean, why come forward after so much time?"

It had been seven years—wasn't that number supposed to be lucky—wonders of the ancient world, the sabbath day of rest, pilgrimage around Mecca, days of the week, continents.

"Who knows?" Tom shrugged. "Maybe he felt guilty. Maybe he was trying to impress the guys in group therapy. Maybe it was part of his 12-step program. Anyway, the girl corroborates his story."

The girl to whom he referred was the mother of the dead infant, herself now 20 years old. At 13, she had delivered a baby alone on a towel in her bedroom while her parents were asleep in the house. No one knew she was pregnant. Not even her boyfriend, the father of the child, now a parolee who had recently admitted this crime.

She cut the umbilical cord with sewing scissors then wrapped her son in sweatpants. He cried and she wadded tissues into his mouth to cover up the sound. Eventually he stopped. The next day, she called her beau to come over. Handing the backpack to him, she told him to take care of it. She had never spoken to anyone else about it. The family had moved from the house two years ago. Tom had told me this on our drive to the scene.

The wind rustled the forest canopy bringing a breeze with a sweet aroma reminiscent of the fresh smell of a baby's skin. I had three sons. Each time I gave birth, I had been ensconced in a hospital bed, free to wail as I roller-coastered between contractions. An epidural arrived just when the pain reached its worst and dulled the unbearable. My husband and doctor coached me through the agony of pushing. Our sons' first cries felt miraculous—sounds of life, survival, continuance.

This mother had been all alone.

"Dr. J?" Tom said, interrupting my reverie. "Should we go ahead and mark out where to dig?"

We walked to the area the young father had indicated. I studied the periwinkle ground cover dotted with purple blooms. Gentle slopes of land mixed with rugged clumps. All appeared undisturbed; I didn't see any sign of a secret grave. There might not be much to see even if I stood on top of it. This would be the smallest cadaver for whom I had ever searched.

"Let's talk with the homeowner," I said.

"Already spoke with him," Tom said. "I didn't give him details, just general info. He knows we're looking for something but that's all. Not who or what or why. He's okay with us going ahead with the investigation."

"Even if it means digging up most of his yard?" I had seen excavations go from small holes to the size of in-ground pools. As searches continued without finding the grave, it became difficult to know when to stop.

"Sure," Tom said, "he told me to do what we need to do."

Everything the youth had told police might be well-intentioned yet misremembered or half-truths. Maybe there was no backpack or sweatpants; the body dumped by itself in a shallow grave. If that were the case, there wouldn't be much left. It could have been dragged off by a coyote, fox, or neighborhood dog. Even if the skeleton remained, it might not be intact but scattered throughout the forest. A newborn had fragile, tiny bones that could easily look like bits of rock or twigs. I worried that the archeological foraging for the child would be in vain.

"That's fine for you to say; you guys are setting up the perimeter. We're doing the digging. I want to talk to the homeowner," I said. We walked back to the house.

Tom knocked on the screen door and called to Mr. Clemons. He joined us on the porch. We shook hands and introduced ourselves.

I went over the basic questions already covered by the detective. The homeowner confirmed that he moved in about one year ago, had done no major construction or landscaping on the property, and didn't know the people who had lived here before.

"Oh, I did add all those bulbs over there," he said. We turned to look at the hundreds of daffodils standing against the edge of the tree line. A cloud dimmed the floral display making it as gray as my mood. I turned to Tom, prepared to talk him out of this Sisyphean hunt.

"I found some bones once. Is that important?" Mr. Clemons said.

I held my breath as if someone had just yelled "red light" in a children's game.

"Could be," Tom said.

"They were real small," Mr. Clemons said. He looked from me to Tom, our faces like statues. "I thought it was an animal. They were wrapped in some cloth and inside a rucksack." He took a deep breath. "I thought it was someone's pet that they buried in the yard. I put it back." He sniffed. "Did I do anything wrong?"

"No, it's probably nothing but every piece of information can be important in an investigation." Tom auto-piloted the answer to calm the man. The description of the burial exactly matched the young man's statement.

"Do you remember where you found them?" I said.

"Over there," he said, pointing to 2 o'clock at the far end of the yard, a long way from the area the young man had indicated.

"Would you mind showing us?" I said.

We walked to the opposite side of the property. The homeowner pointed to a maple tree, appearing like every other one in the woods.

"I'm sure it's right about here," he said. "See how the bulbs are spread?" Some of the daffodils looked like they had strayed from their chorus line.

"I tried not to disturb the grave. Beloved family pet and all," he said. "It wasn't far down. Two, maybe two and a half feet."

The location Mr. Clemons provided seemed more viable for a search than the young father's recollection from his teen years. We planned to begin at this spot.

It took the rest of the day to coordinate the team, forensic investigators from my office and a university anthropologist. The police set up a crime scene perimeter and guarded it that night.

The next morning at dawn we set up a tent as a shelter from the elements and onlookers. We marked out a ten-foot by ten-foot grid. Four of us worked; each starting in a different corner. We used hand trowels to uncover the top coating of soil. Then we sifted the dirt through fine mesh. This scientific technique conserved any fragment we might find of such a tiny person. The digging progressed slowly. Each bit of stone or stick required professional examination.

One of my investigators specialized in skeletons and had received advanced training. Ron led many of the MEO excavations. He spearheaded the identification of any bony material brought to our office. His dedication made this work a little easier.

After 11 hours, Ron said, "I got something."

He placed a small stake to identify the spot. The team formed a huddle. Something dark poked up from the exposed ground. Two workers bent down and brushed away the residue, unmasking the shoulder straps of a knapsack. It took another hour to clear away debris to see the pack clearly. A portion of the backside had disintegrated but enough of it remained to cushion the baby.

The contents peeked through. The sweatpants had been reduced to threads, dulled cotton fibers that clung to white bone. I recognized the sections of skull—frontal, temporal, parietal, occipital—definitely human.

We excavated a space beneath the backpack and moved a wood panel under it for support. Ron helped place the wood and the bag into a cardboard box. We sealed it with tape, signed and dated it, all to maintain the evidence.

The next part of the examination would take place at the morgue—x-rays, toxicology testing, and DNA studies. The anthropologist and I would look for trauma in the skeleton and attempt to identify the 300 newborn bones that had laid in the earth for seven years, longer than my youngest son had walked upon it.

I carried the box past the homeowner, the police, and the neighbors gathered on the sidewalk. Spring break had brought out an assortment of children, dog walkers, and strollers. A news reporter snapped a photo. The box felt impossibly light. Even with the knapsack and the brace, it weighed less than each of my sons at birth.

Ron opened the trunk of the car, and we laid the carton inside. The long dead remains were surrounded by fabric, wood, and cardboard—sheets of protection for a life never lived. I looked at my hands, dirt under the nails, grime smeared on my watch face obscuring the time.

Triumph over finding the body frayed like the child's fabric coffin. My sense of fulfillment, of a job well-done, collapsed.

This unexpected family reunion would result in a trial and more sorrow. The young girl and her son had been linked in pain and separated by desperation. I drove to the office with the infant cocooned in the back of the Jeep.

Vesey Street

The temporary morgue for the World Trade Center Disaster sat at 235 Vesey Street in New York City, 250 miles from my home in Syracuse.

We collected remnants of bodies: arms and legs and helmets that held only skulls, to try to identify the dead. Nearly 3,000 people had died. As the chief pathologist from DMORT tasked with recognizing human remains and preparing them for transport to the NYC Medical Examiner's Office, I spent my days sifting what the firefighters brought in from the rubble.

Pieces of yellow, white, and pink paper floated in the air like slow motion confetti. I stooped to pick up one of the larger fragments with black lettering—"Dun & Bradstreet." Important words in another time, a disconnected piece of a jigsaw puzzle that would never be put back together; like the human remains that confronted me.

Thick, gray/brown, acrid smoke rose continuously from the huge burning pyre a block away. The scent of fire hung on my clothes even after I returned to my hotel bed at night, the fumes still there the next day.

As I stood outside the tent, my exhaling breath condensed in the air. I was cold, clad only in a short-sleeve green polo and khaki pants, the weather unseasonably chilly for a September morning.

I heard a thumping overhead and saw a helicopter flying in a low circle around the grounds. Despite the restricted airspace, these Sikorskys were a familiar sight here at Ground Zero. *Thwomp, thwomp, thwomp,*

thwomp. The rhythmic beating of the blades broke the stillness of the early post dawn. I shivered, from the temperature and the sound.

I walked toward the porta-potty across the street, stepping over concrete and metal debris. A path had been cleared down the center of this once-busy urban block allowing rescue vehicles and hearses through. Much of the refuse remained pushed to the sides.

Across the street, a cavity in the ground yawned 50 feet in length and width. Cars had been towed there and stacked; covered in dust and crushed in on the tops. Tires were flattened and windows smashed appearing as if they had been looted. Thousands were still without power in this part of the city.

"I need to see your ID," a stern-looking, much-too-young soldier said as he put his hand up to stop me. The other hand held an M16 rifle. I was surprised at this added security since I had already passed 13 checkpoints to get there.

Past the Family Assistance Center with walls covered in pictures of young fathers with kids piled on their laps, smiling pregnant women, brothers and sisters with arms entwined in a reunion, wedding photos, current and old.

Past prayer vigils with groups of people huddled on blankets, lighting candles, and holding up banners for peace.

Past evangelists with flyers that read "Come home to Jesus" and proclaimed the end of the world.

Past the Manhattan Medical Examiner's Office with tables of human remains outside its building, in the alley between NYU and the morgue, sheets draping the ominous contents.

Past barricaded streets filled with lines of people stretching for two blocks, young and old coming out every morning; some spending the night.

Closer to the site, police officers kept them out of the street beyond the wooden sawhorses like at a celebratory parade. These folks handed out bottled water and candy, waved flags and cheered us on. Their faces were so hopeful; at times I couldn't bear to look at them.

These civilians thought living people would be found in the destroyed earth. To them we were performing a rescue mission. It never had been that, not really. Our goal was to recover the dead, to look at the bits and pieces left after the bodies had rained down from great heights.

I pulled the lanyard with my ID from beneath my shirt, kept there to prevent it dipping into blood and grime as I worked in the temporary morgue.

"Thank you, ma'am," the soldier said and resumed his guard.

The toilet door creaked as I opened it—an eerie sound like in *Radio Mystery Theater*. I unbuckled my belt and eased my pants slowly down. The pockets filled with equipment—flashlight, ruler, Swiss army knife, clean gloves, markers, labels, notepad—clunked to the ground. The frigid edge of the latrine raised the hairs on my skin. The cold minimized the outhouse smell.

My pee sounded desolate as my bladder emptied the first of many coffees of the day. I had learned to drink it any way available: black, with sugar or cream, with both, with artificial creamer, cold, lukewarm, hot, but never decaf. Caffeine was fuel for my constantly exhausted body.

I finished, readjusted myself, and pulled out a small bottle of hand sanitizer from my back pocket and squirted some onto my hands and made a note to tell the supply officer that the lavatories needed some. Small duties kept a sense of order amidst the despair of chaos.

As I approached the tent, a man dressed exactly like me emerged. Taller and many years my junior, he smiled warmly.

"Hey, I was looking for you," Elias said.

"Just using the head," I said.

"I brought some breakfast sandwiches. They had them in the Red Cross trailer." He handed me one.

I didn't have much of an appetite, but politely took the proffered gift. Elias started to take a bite and then watched me as I stared at the sandwich.

"Hey, what's up?" he said.

The wind gusted, causing the office confetti to swirl around our boot-clad feet, together with irregular fragments of ash. Two weeks after the attack and the fires still burned.

"The bathrooms are closed," I said, referring to the building next to our morgue. It had had the nicest lavatories. After the attack some Vietnam Vets had cleaned them up, lining scented candles on the counters and supplying personal hygiene articles, toilet paper, and paper towels. There was running water and clean toilets. Now they were shuttered.

"Why?" he said.

I pointed to a new 20-foot-long fissure in the gap between the sidewalk and this building next door.

"This crack appeared. I heard someone say there are falling beams inside. Now the building is considered unstable and unsafe to enter."

Every few minutes for the past two days, I had felt a vibration in my zipper, belt buckle, and the badge in my pocket as the cranes removed the steel beams at the site; their demolition shook the earth.

On the outer wall of this edifice another warning, spray painted in orange, read "Three loud blasts = Evacuation."

"That sign is also helpful," I said pointing to the orange graffiti.

"Yeah, if you hear those blasts, run to the Hudson River and jump in."

The great military presence in the city and a government working hard to keep us safe had informed us of this. There was no more sophisticated plan for evacuating than RUN. Every day there were rumors of another attack. We received daily updates—"Do not leave a van unattended - it can be used as a weapon" and "Report any suspicious activity. We are in the midst of a war."

We stood in silence for a few moments holding onto our food. The enormity washed over me.

"Did you see your bucket?" Elias pointed toward the front of the tent. The warning label on the white 5-gallon container stood out among the gray concrete. In English and Spanish, it advised keeping children away, noting the danger with even a small amount of water. My words returned from more than a decade earlier.

"At least there's a warning that worked," he said. I inhaled that thought, took it deep into my lungs.

"We speak for the dead," I said. "To help the living."

Elias nodded.

"Dr. J?" A man poked his head out of the tent, a police detective in another world.

"Yes?" I said.

"We have incoming."

"Be right there." I put the uneaten meal into my pocket.

I paused to look at a large, metal sculpture that had, against the odds, survived. Ten-foot-tall figures held up signs for New York and Quebec with square panels in their abdomens painted light blue and bordered by white clouds. The statue promised the opportunity of flight.

Instead, people had fallen out of the sky.

The Package

"PLEASE help her," the woman said as she approached the tent.

The wind picked up a bit, making words that followed hard to hear. Dust and debris floated in the air like being near a huge bonfire.

No signage or name existed on the tent, but everyone knew its purpose —the temporary morgue at Ground Zero of the World Trade Center.

Choppers hovered overhead reminding us of tight security, a continued threat to the site, and the nearness of war.

The woman wore a firefighter's uniform sans the helmet. The outfit enveloped her; pale hands stuck out of the overhanging sleeves. Soot smeared her face. She gripped a football-sized object, covering the bundle with her arms. I saw the top of it—wispy red-brown material. The woman's hair matched this and was short and tidy where it had been protected under a helmet. She planted herself six feet away from the entrance and clutched the item to her chest. I imagined if I got any closer, she would growl at me.

"Okay, let's see," the man seated at the intake desk said.

He motioned her forward with his hand. The woman came no nearer. The man looked down at paperwork, maybe hoping to find the protocol for this situation. The federal government had a response for everything.

"I found her," the woman said.

She cradled the object in her arms, supporting it like it was a newborn. The receptionist beckoned for another team member to greet the woman. As the second man approached, the woman stepped back. She turned sideways, shielding the package from others. She moved like a feral mother.

"I found her," the woman said, rocking her treasure.

Both men started speaking at once.

"Just let us have it."

"We'll take care of everything."

For weeks, exhausted firefighters had been battling the fires of the debris pile that had once been the tallest human-made structures in the world. Smoky haze still obscured the sun and the outlines of the surviving skyscrapers. As soon as one conflagration was extinguished, another would erupt. High temperatures in the ruins caused flammable material to continually spark.

The fire department was in charge of the scene because as an active fire, it threatened life and property. The police were not in charge though the site was an active crime scene. The federal government was not in charge though the destruction was caused by terrorists. The fire department had full responsibility to put out the conflagration.

The same firefighters who had rushed in to save the victims caught in the jet fuel inferno and collapse of concrete and girders were now recovering the corpses.

In the first few days after the planes had hit the towers, intact bodies surfaced. Heads and limbs had been traumatized but were attached to chests and spines. As the disaster site continued to burn and the searching went deeper, only pieces were recovered—a portion of skull attached to a helmet, an amputated arm, a disembodied foot. Men and women battled the earth to relinquish its hold on their brothers and sisters in arms and then carried them to our morgue.

Any scrap of material associated with rescue workers, not civilians, furthered the urgency of whatever they found. Four or five firefighters routinely came into the tent, bypassing the intake desk, and demanded my attention.

"This could be Captain Smith's helmet," one would say. "I can see the numbers three and four on it. His number was 344."

Looking up from whatever I was already doing, I said, "Okay, I'm going to check that right away. Follow me."

Then I headed back to the anteroom and nodded to the priest to say a few words. The attendant began the paperwork. The group hovered at my shoulder. We returned to the exam room. They barely left any room for me to move my arms as I inspected whatever object or bit of a person lay on the gurney. Their breathing whispered in my ears. I felt the heat emanating from their clothes and smelled burned wood, metal, and fear.

An organized system prevailed: material logged, tagged, and ceremoniously placed on a table in an anteroom until my team was ready. A clergy person—priest, minister, or rabbi—said a benediction over the possible remains.

Once transferred to my station the scientific examination began. Our team of pathologist and anthropologist decided if the specimen was human or not and, if not, whether it was personal effects belonging to someone killed that day. We processed a lot of trash material—chicken wings, pork ribs, vermin—and thousands of body parts.

The day the woman arrived with her package had been a day like all the others that had preceded it.

"I want to help. Let me just take a look," I said, stepping slowly toward her.

She shook her head and swayed on her feet.

"Could someone get this woman a seat?" I said. A folding chair materialized next to the woman. "Go ahead, sit down and rest a little."

Workers from both tents had gathered behind me in the anteroom. I waved them back. The priest clutched his hands together. I could hear him saying the Lord's Prayer.

The woman sat, her posture relaxing after the effort of supporting the article. She had probably been on her feet the past 12 hours. She might not have slept for days.

"Why don't you let me examine your friend, I might be able to help you," I said. I didn't feel equipped for psychological intercession. A police department hostage negotiator hovered behind me, out of his realm as well.

Only six feet separated the woman and me. I decreased the distance by inches first to four and then two feet. A tear streaked through the soot on her face.

"Thanks for all your hard work," I said. "I'm sure she appreciates it. I'll take her now." I stood very close and reached out my arms.

She stared a long time at the cherished possession then looked up and held my gaze. I received the object with both hands, then imitated her posture of holding a baby. It was unbearably light and might float away if I didn't hold on tight enough.

"Thank you," I said.

She hadn't said anything else. An assistant came over and offered her tissues and a bottle of water. The other intake worker assigned the case a number and prepared labels. Someone spread a blanket on the nearest gurney to protect the item from the cold steel. The priest said a blessing.

I laid the parcel down. My team and I stared at a synthetic red wig attached to a scalp protector. It wasn't human. It hadn't been damaged by fire or blood or weather. It wasn't from the events of September 11th. My back was to the woman, but I could hear her sobbing.

I wondered where the woman had found it. I might never know. Rescue workers weren't specific about where they recovered the remains even when they brought in an actual body part. They moved with haste to bring their fallen comrades to us, carrying urgency and possible pieces of humans. Provenance was lost.

We wrapped up the wig with the blanket, not wanting to throw it out in front of the woman. I didn't know what would happen to her, if she would be removed from duty, given psychological counseling, or assisted home.

I told her the bundle wasn't human. She wept.

Dead End

"Mom, why are all the police cars and fire trucks here?" David, then 13, had asked.

"What did you say, honey?" I said, covering my free ear. "Police? Fire trucks?"

Brrring. Brrring. Brrring.

Another phone line at the reception counter rang loudly making it difficult to hear. I gestured to my co-workers to lower the volume. A quick reply of silence followed. They listened to the boss.

I had taken the call at the front desk extension. It was the fifth time David had called me at work that day. He was home with a fever and sore throat. Large tonsils made him prone to *strep* infections. I had already advised him on what to eat, what DVDs to watch, when to take Tylenol, and how to make a fruit smoothie. I glanced at my watch—1 p.m.

"Are you okay?"

"Yeah," David said. "I can't see what they're doing. I want to go outside. Why are they here? There's no smoke. Everybody is at the dead end." He strung the phrases together like a puka necklace with no space between the shell disks.

The cause for the emergency response eluded me. We lived on a private lane. Occasionally, a pet dog got loose.

"Can I go see Miss Teddy?" he asked, referring to our elderly next-door neighbor. At 91, she still lived alone and maintained an independent life. My son often went to see her after school even at the cusp of adolescence. What would greet him today? The first responders must be for her.

"I'll be right home. Stay in the house with Baba," I said gathering up my keys and jacket. I knew she had made him chicken soup, Jewish penicillin. "You don't want to get Miss Teddy sick."

"Dr. J," called the receptionist as she waved a message slip in her hand.

"I have to go. Emergency at home. I'll call you when I get there," I said.

The route to my house unspooled in front of me like a roll of cotton gauze. I drove quickly, worried about my neighbor, staying just over the speed limit not wanting a ticket and the delay. In my rush, I hadn't connected my hands-free phone device so I couldn't call David, Miss Teddy, or my office without stopping. Siri wasn't born yet. I kept going.

Staccato images of Miss Teddy resonated as I headed home.

This pioneer of the community had welcomed us with an orchid from her greenhouse when we arrived in town a decade earlier. Invitations to visit followed. We shared dinners at each other's homes.

When my mother died, in addition to Baba, Miss Teddy became an alternate grandmother. Our neighbor's two grown daughters lived far away. She had been widowed for 20 years. The relationship between us grew with symbiotic intimacy.

"I built this house after my husband passed away," she informed me. "The name on the sign is 'Evergreen', for all the pines here. Still, I like to think of it as 'Serendipity.'" Miss Teddy saw our connection that way and was forever grateful to the circumstance around her.

The day she met David, not long after we moved in, she had puttered into our driveway in an open golf-cart. As I unloaded groceries from the station wagon, David ran over to her. She shut the engine off and stood up. Her spine remained at a 45-degree angle with the ground.

"What's wrong with your back?" David asked. "You look like that hunchback guy." This was the curse of reading *Illustrated Classics* to this precocious preschooler.

“David,” I said, “that’s not polite. I’m sorry, Miss Teddy.”

The old woman eyed him and said, “Hop on and I’ll tell you all about it.”

A bond formed that day, special to the two of them. She enjoyed his curiosity and forthright attitude, qualities she shared. He visited her and played checkers. They surveyed the forest animals through binoculars. She shared her artistic projects with him—objet d’art lamps and Scandinavian wooden trays decorated with stylized flowers. Their creative spirits had synergy.

She liked reciting poetry, her own and those remembered from her one-room schoolhouse. Her raised-bed garden produced an abundance of pole beans in the summer. Hummingbirds crowded outside the large picture window in her den. Echoes of “Here Dickie, Dickie, Dickie” rang out in the evenings as she called her golden retriever home.

She and I talked of spouses—both of ours were physicians.

“It’s a wonder,” she said, “you’re at the job all hours, and your husband cooks.” She shook her head. “You’ve got things turned around, but it works.” She marveled at my ability to have a career and a family. She had given up Occupational Therapy to raise her children.

The fear of losing her coalesced into a focus of pain, like a bee sting unattended, the barb left in the skin.

I’d imagined she would live forever, but no one does. I saw that at my job every day. Dying causes shock and sadness in the moment, even if expected. I was not prepared to confront it as I reached my street.

A large ladder truck, a sheriff’s SUV, an ambulance, and two town police cars were parked nearby. Further out, television crews had set up high reception towers near the intersection. The scene was like hundreds of others but the location, comfortable and serene, had morphed into the peculiar. My professional and personal lives collided.

A patrol officer approached as I eased behind the fire engine, closer than he had allowed the reporters.

"Miss, you can't park here," he said, holding up his palm to me.

I stepped from the car, flipped open my badge, and walked past him without a word.

The chief of police approached, extending his hand.

"We just notified your office," Gene said. "How did you get here so fast, Doc?"

"My son called me. He was home today. I live right there," I said. My palm was sweaty as I returned the handshake.

Gene's eyes turned to gaze at my house. I felt nauseated. Responding to my neighborhood as a civilian had officially transformed into duty.

"What is this about? Did she fall? Was there a fire? A home invasion?" I said. All the possibilities were draped in violence.

"No." Gene sounded confused.

We looked at each other. I scrutinized the view. One cop stood in the road with a long measuring tape. The EMTs leaned against the ambulance. Firefighters gathered with large equipment at the end of the road. My vision sharpened. Through the trees, I could see Miss Teddy on her front porch, only ten yards and not a celestial world away. I stood straighter. She waved. I smiled and waved back.

A checklist of happy future times replaced the blank sheet of a moment ago. Miss Teddy scaring the kids at Halloween as she proffered candy from her creepy extendable hand. Thanksgiving dinner including her homemade biscuits would complete our family table. Her daughters might enjoy spiked eggnog at a Christmas visit. Relief infused me.

Gene described the accident—single vehicle to fixed object as it was known in police vernacular. A teenager had died. The boy, driving alone, had flipped the car at the end of the street about three in the morning, trying to achieve zero to 60 mph in less than six seconds as advertised in the TV commercial.

The sky darkened. Guilt rimmed the periphery of my solace.

"How old?" I asked.

"Sixteen," the Chief said.

Joshua was 15. Soon he would be eligible for a permit under NY laws, but not under my house rules; my sons wouldn't get their driving privileges until they turned 18.

"From around here?"

"No." Gene named a town miles away.

I closed my eyes. Did the teen even have a real license or just a learner's permit? Where had he been? Where was he going? Was he even familiar with the neighborhood? Questions his family would agonize over in the days to come.

"Parents notified?" I thought of the unimaginable.

"Yeah, one of my guys is on the way to their house, but they may see it on the news first." He gestured to the towers on the road.

"We can't let that happen. Get the privacy screen. Please."

Gene handed me the PPE I needed then radioed his team. We moved along the path to the site of the wreck.

The cul-de-sac consisted of a circular turn-around with split logs at the edge of the roadway marking the perimeter. The street ended abruptly. No lamps illuminated the area. All the suburban houses were dark at night. Later, I would check a lunar chart and realize the waxing crescent moon had provided very little illumination. Gloom enveloped the teen with no way out.

Black streaks coursed on the asphalt surface where the car braked prior to the collision. The tires struck the wooded border; the car became airborne before impact with the tree. I stepped through the brambles and limestone in the rut beyond the dead end.

A red Mustang lay upside down. The roof crushed into the earth. The engine block had cracked from hitting a 100-year-old maple. A large gouge marked the spot at eight feet up from the base of the tree. I heard Gene breathing behind me. Red and blue lights fractured the atmosphere in rhythmic waves. The air smelled damp.

I saw the boy through the broken windows on the driver's side. His body upside down and seat-belted in place dangled like a puppet. White powder dotted his chest from the exploded airbag. Dried blood coated the beige fabric of the seat.

"Did you hear anything in the night?" Gene said.

I rewound my evening—chicken dinner, homework review, stories before bedtime, office reports, conversation with Marc, asleep by 10:30 p.m. Had it stormed last night, thundered? I bent down to touch the dry ground. I had slept uninterrupted until the daily alarm at six. David hadn't felt ill until the morning. There had been no nightmares, no requests for water, no midnight refrigerator raids, no telephone calls from the office. It had been a very calm night.

The crash must have made a monstrous boom in the wee hours. I looked in the direction of my home, not visible from this angle. Had the overlay of the tree canopy muffled the noise?

"No," I said. "Nothing. I don't think anyone in my family did either. Nobody said anything at breakfast, but I'll check with them."

"I talked to the lady in the house over there." Gene pointed to Serendipity. "Her bedroom is about 50 feet away. She's amazing."

I nodded slightly; my head felt too heavy to do much more.

"She said she heard a loud bang at 2:45 a.m.," he continued. "She actually put on her glasses and looked at the clock. It took her about 10 minutes to get out of bed and make her way to the front door. Said she stood there yelling for a while asking if everybody was okay but didn't hear anything else. She couldn't see much in the dark from her front porch. There were no car lights, nothing. She thought it must have been some kids fooling around along the power line ease-way."

This stalwart woman, spine angled acutely due to osteoporosis, hearing the thunderous sound had painstakingly gone outside in the middle of the night to see if she could help.

"She's a reliable witness," I said.

"Sure is."

Miss Teddy had responded. I slept on. The boy lingered alone.

A warmth spread from my neck upwards. My feet stiffened in my work boots. The surgical gloves tightened around my fingers. I breathed deeply, mouth closed, counting to four with each inhalation. Wind gusted in the stillness causing a few leaves to drop.

"How did you find the car?" I asked, "It's camouflaged in the gully."

"When he didn't show up home last night, the mom called around. Friends had seen him speed off in this direction after dropping them off down the street near the intersection. Said they didn't hear anything. They went out searching today. Found him here." Gene looked down as if studying his shoes for the quality of polish.

"Hmm," I said, pondering the sound, the night, the friends. "Our office will have to talk to the parents. We'll do x-rays and toxicology tests. After that the autopsy will be first thing in the morning." I stripped off the gloves, booties, and mask.

We shook hands again.

"Thanks, you got it from here. I'm going to say hello to your witness now," I said.

Miss Teddy observed the scene from her usual afternoon post on a stone bench by her front door. Gravel crunched underfoot as I approached. She raised her right hand that held an empty tumbler. I took it wordlessly and headed inside the familiar abode.

I called David to reassure him that Miss Teddy was fine. He could come visit when he felt better. I updated my office and signed off for the day.

Arriving at the cabinet that housed the gin and tonic, I replayed Miss Teddy's instructions on how to prepare the classic British drink. Every day at 5 p.m. she had this restorative.

"How much gin?" I once asked her.

"Just count to three," she had said, demonstrating with the closed Tanqueray bottle. "One, two, three, for a good day." She poured quickly. Then, she poured again, this time more slowly. "One. Two. Three. For a rough one."

I used the more languid technique distributing the liquor into two glasses, then added a generous splash of tonic. A fresh-cut lime on the bar along with a few softening ice cubes finished the recipe. Returning to the porch, I handed one to my friend and sat down. Side by side, our hips touching, we watched the recovery workers.

The sound of metal crunching and scraping filled the air as machinery opened the car to extricate the boy's body. The Jaws of Life were at work—designed to scissor open automotive metal and save an injured occupant. A misnomer for me as I never saw its life-saving capabilities.

Her gnarled hand reached over and patted my thigh. I took her fingers in mine and squeezed them lightly.

"Thanks," I said.

Her blue eyes were rheumy.

"I thought it was just kids out hot-rodding." Her voice quavered, unlike her usual speech.

"I didn't hear a thing. Not a sound," I said. The confession made me teary.

We sipped our G&Ts as the investigators finished up their tasks.

The trucks drove away, leaving Miss Teddy and me alone in a world with a shattered afternoon. I put my head on her shoulder. Feathery white hair tickled my forehead. The softness of her cashmere sweater brushed my face.

"I thought it was you," I whispered.

"I know." She cleared her throat.

I expected a poetry recitation, maybe Longfellow's "The Sound of the Sea" might be apropos with "A voice out of the silence of the deep" and "Are divine foreshadowing and foreseeing / Of things beyond our reason and control."

Instead, silently she leaned her head onto mine. We contemplated the ice melting in our glasses.

Dinner Hour

"What's for supper?" I said. I had phoned home after finishing my last case of the day.

Light filtered through the opaque security windows of the morgue at the Syracuse Medical Examiner's Office promising a clear summer evening. I wanted to shed my PPE and shower.

"You tell me," Marc said.

The habit of conferring with me about the dinner menu was ingrained in him. Though, as the primary cook of the family, he could have made those executive decisions.

I looked over at the technician who was zipping up the body bag of the victim of a house fire. The aroma of charcoal hung in the air.

"Not barbecue," I said.

Marc sighed. Lengthening summer days, temperatures in the 70s, and the Adirondack picnic table outside our house beckoned to him.

"Oh yeah, there was that fire in Cicero." He paused. I imagined he already had the grill ready to go. Then in a brighter voice, he added, "The chicken can wait. How about tuna salad?" We would still have our outdoor picnic.

"Sure, that works."

I wasn't your typical picky eater: no dietary restrictions, allergies, sensitivities, even dislikes. Yet, I often avoided foods that evoked remembrances of the day. They made me nauseous.

No rice if there had been a case with maggots. No boned beef (steak, ribs) if there had been a severe car accident. Nothing similar to anything

I saw in the stomachs of the day, which were a gastric mélange. I avoided organ meat: brain, kidneys, pancreas, liver.

Marc never complained about my abstinences. After spending time in the kitchen preparing a nice meal, he didn't want to watch me push the food around my plate to avoid the offending item. He learned to ask first.

Marc is an ophthalmologist. The most blood he ever sees from his patients comes during surgery when the anesthetist places an intravenous line. The eye is pristine, sheltered, and separated from the gore of the rest of the body. He is in the cleanest field of medicine while I toiled in the dirtiest.

He caught glimpses of my world from open textbooks or computer screens as I studied for boards or prepared a lecture. The corporeal horror of it was left to his imagination.

Seneca the Stoic philosopher said, "We suffer more often in imagination than in reality." Maybe for others, this was true. Reality pained mine.

During my first month in fellowship training, Marc picked me up from the Cook County MEO. The morgue attendant addressed him as Dr. Jumbelic. Marc didn't correct the man, instead he smiled. I often expressed more umbrage if someone called me Mrs. Safran or asked me my maiden name, replying "I've never been a maiden." Marc was flattered to be called by my name. He took pride in me and whenever he introduced me as his wife, said my full name. He's sweet that way.

"Hey, honey," I said, greeting him in the intake area and kissing him on the cheek.

"Aww" the techs chorused. Our gold wedding bands seemed to catch the light of the overhead fluorescents. We hadn't yet celebrated our one-year wedding anniversary.

"I just have to grab a book," I said. I had already showered the detritus of the day away before our date at our favorite Thai restaurant, PS Bangkok. Marc followed me into the morgue.

He stopped at the doorway. Four dead people lay in body bags on the gurneys. He saw two more corpses through the windows to the second autopsy suite. All the dissections were done. The technicians had cleaned up and were preparing to put everybody back in the cooler.

Marc's face paled; tiny droplets of sweat rose on his brow.

My first view of a morgue had been less sanitized: the guts, buckets, and blood. This seemed more like a surgical operating room in comparison. I didn't point this out to him.

Finally, he said, "This looks like an auto garage."

Carl opened a large metal door. The huge cooler emitted cold air into the room. The refrigerated unit had the capacity to hold over a hundred bodies. Shelves extended floor to ceiling, row after row. We had a manual pallet jack to reach the bodies near the top. The corpses that spent a lot of time with us—unidentified remains and complicated homicides—rested in cardboard caskets awaiting release. The most recent cases were positioned no higher than shoulder level. Moving dead weight had pulled out many a worker's back.

"Wow, you work on the body just like it's a car," Marc said, sticking with the auto shop analogy. We did find out what went wrong but didn't do body repair.

During that first year of training, cutting into skin, fat, muscle, and organs, I developed an aversion to meat. I remained a vegetarian for the duration of my fellowship. My non-meat diet eventually waned but I began selectively rejecting food.

My dietary specifications were usually limited to the evening after my case and dissipated by morning. Marc never argued with the logic of my choices. He avoided whatever was bothering me that day, even if it meant a trip to the grocery store to change out the main course.

I suppose if I had been the chef, it would have been easier, but Marc loved the artistry and science of cooking. He is a gourmet and a gourmand. He also arrived home an hour before me and utilized the time to make dinner.

This mealtime became sacred to us. Whatever the demands on our schedules—work, education, after-school activities—as parents we cherished the ritual which brought all the family together in the same room. We lingered, talking of classes, homework, sports, current affairs, upcoming weekend events, and chauffeuring responsibilities.

As the boys got older, they heard news from the radio on the bus, or from classmates watching TV. We didn't have cable television and had no signal for the local stations. Inevitably our kids heard from friends or teachers about MEO cases. At dinner hour, they asked questions. I protected them from the gory details but answered them as I might a reporter, sharing public but not privileged information. They were fascinated.

Once when some middle school friends were at the house, someone asked David what I did for a living.

"She cuts up dead people," David said, emphasizing the word, dead. "She's a real doctor."

I jumped in to soften the blunt description.

"I investigate and do autopsies, which are like surgeries, so I can explain to families and police why someone died."

"Wow," the friends chorused.

David was right. I cut up dead people and because of this I couldn't have certain foods for dinner. Corn salsa? No, thanks. That fibrous kernel of goodness lasts for a long time in the bowel. Pasta? No. The barely digested spaghetti in the stomach of a young man lingered in my mind. Beer? Nah. The latest hadn't even been absorbed by the decedent.

After I retired, I became the primary cook at home. It didn't seem fair to Marc who worked a full day when I had free time. The visceral images of the morgue dissipated—ribs were from a pig or cow, rice was a starch from a waterlogged field, and beer came from a brewery. I enjoyed myself. My signature dish, Coriander Chicken, remains a favorite: fatty thighs with the bones still in, slathered with toasted coriander, salt, and sesame oil.

When COVID hit, the pendulum swung again. Adult children returned home, along with quarantine and isolation. Marc's office closed for two months. He began cooking again and then kept the job as home chef even after returning to work.

His fanciest meals are served on Sundays when we have all the boys (and their partners) for a traditional family dinner. We serve appetizers and a themed drink while the grand dogs race around the house. For the main dish, we usually have meat (brisket, ribs, or roast turkey) with root veggies in the winter and fresh salad in the summer. Dessert follows in the form of homemade ice cream or gelato.

The conversation flows—health, vacations, news, friends, jobs, houses —reminding me of dinner hour long ago. Sometimes we play a board or lawn game before everyone goes back home.

Marc and I have developed a symbiotic system during our 36 years of marriage. It manifests in the dinner hour as he cooks, and I set up and clean. These tasks suit us. It mirrors the way we've approached our lives: supporting and filling in the gaps.

The Taking Tree

The man sat in the lawn chair facing the tall maple tree; dried blood formed a circle around his feet.

"Mr. Andris?" I said.

He remained with hands in his lap, in repose like a busker in a tableau vivant. Edgar hadn't left this spot since the morgue transport took Kristine away a day earlier.

"I'm Dr. Jumbelic. I'm sorry for the death of your wife," I said. He shivered as the words stung him like alcohol on a fresh scrape.

A ladder rested against the trunk with a handsaw set nearby. The equipment might have been waiting for the man to return to Saturday chores. The only hint of trauma resided in a latex glove peeking out among fallen yellow leaves. That and the sanguinous patch on the ground.

The couple had been working together, as they did most weekends. She steadied the ladder while he sawed a tree limb. The bough cracked and struck her in the head. Kristine had landed on the ground in the same location in which Edgar now sat. The offending branch, as thick as the man's thigh, lay prostrate beside him, both their insides brittle.

Parallels of sun and shade obscured Edgar's face. His pate showed balding rimmed by white hair. He wore a flannel shirt unbuttoned at the collar and spilling out of his jeans. Smears of red stained the pants and sleeves where he had cradled the head of his wife of 50 years.

The wind brought the feel of winter. Edgar had kept his overnight vigil despite chilling temperatures.

"Edgar," I said, "you told my investigator that you wanted to speak to me."

He looked up—red lids accentuated the green of his irises. Veins bloomed on his cheeks. He spoke through dried lips.

"Yes," he said, "I do." The phrase felt like a levee containing a floodplain of grief.

On the drive from the office, I had considered what I could say to this man. I often talked to families at the scenes or met with them later to discuss autopsy results. Did he want the details of how Kristine's scalp split open, her skull fractured, and her brain crushed? What did Edgar desire to know that he hadn't already seen?

"Her spirit's here," he said. "I can't leave yet. There's something I need to ask you."

I waited. Geese honked as they trekked south. Dried foliage danced with the breeze. A squirrel chittered as it ran past.

"Was it quick?" he finally said.

"Yes," I said. Kristine had no pulse or respiration when the paramedics arrived four minutes after the emergency call.

Edgar folded in on himself as if the unasked question had been holding him upright.

I stared at the tree.

As each autumn leaf fell, a year of Edgar and Kristine's lives together seemed to pass. One. Two. Three. A gust and ten dropped. I counted until I reached their golden anniversary.

Stairwell

A crowd gathered outside as Joe watched through a grimy kitchen window. People huddled in groups of twos and threes facing a deserted apartment building. Joe scanned the area then checked the time on the microwave—7:00 a.m. Folks were getting ready to leave for work. He didn't recognize most of them; he had moved to Syracuse only recently. Besides, night shifts in the warehouse prevented him from crossing paths with normal day jobbers.

The cloudless sky formed shadows on the cemented yard. Joe stubbed out a cigarette in the foil ashtray and hurried to join the spectators. October air chilled his bare arms. He had forgotten a jacket in his haste.

This was how Joe described the scene to me later when I interviewed him.

The onlookers held their ground as Joe pushed through. He felt desperate to get to the front of the queue. Each person expectantly watched the dwelling, like paparazzi hoping to glimpse a celebrity.

Graffitied plywood covered the first-floor windows. Broken glass panes decorated the second and third levels. Gutters dangled from eaves; limbs amputated before reaching the ground.

"Hey," Joe said, waving at a police officer guarding the back door of the house of interest. Yellow crime-scene tape surrounded it for some 15 feet. The cop stared into the distance, hands crossed in front, at attention. A dog barked, insistent and deep.

Joe ran his right hand through his thinning blonde hair, then along the edges of his thick, graying mustache. Joe listened to the hum of conversation at this unexpected mid-week excitement:

"Found her this morning."

"Bottom of the stairs, I heard."

"A fall maybe?

"Who is she?"

"Betcha it was Nelly's girl."

"Must have been drugs."

"You don't know that."

Joe's pulse thumped in his ears, blood pressure rising. He had forgotten to take his pills last night. Maybe the night before, too. Dizzy with panic, he considered going back to his apartment for the medicine. He discarded the idea.

"Hey," Joe said more loudly, motioning again to get the officer's attention. "Excuse me, sir, what's going on?" He aimed for a civil tone but ended up shouting over the buzz of the crowd.

The cop maintained a rigid posture, like a statue.

Joe tapped the shoulder of a tall, black man standing in front of him. Despite the cool temperature, Joe's hands were sweating. Back muscles tensed at Joe's touch. The thought that Joe might stain the man's fine suit distracted him. The man rotated his head a few degrees in Joe's direction.

"Sorry," Joe said. "Do you know what this is about? Can you see anything?"

The man turned fully toward Joe. They were about the same age, mid-forties. It was the only trait they shared. Towering over Joe's diminutive frame, this person exuded confidence and power.

"Do I know you?" the man said.

The man's sunglasses mirrored Joe's reflection—hair unwashed, cheeks shadowed, and body shivering. Joe hadn't eaten, hadn't slept, and had smoked four packs of cigarettes since Sunday. He'd missed work for two nights calling family, friends, and everyone from his contact list. No one knew where Lashana had gone. Fear stopped him from calling the police. Joe flushed red as he shook his head.

"I heard they found somebody in there," Joe said. He gestured toward the scuffed door of the nearby aging construction.

The two men stared at each other; eyes unwavering. Joe had been in this situation before—no connections, out of place, black versus white. Honesty worked best.

"I'll be straight with you, man. It's my wife," Joe said. "I'm scared it's her in there."

The man removed his glasses. His voice gained a deeper timbre.

"They found a woman in there early this morning," he said. "African American." He pronounced each word distinctly. "Woman in her thirties." He weighed his next statement. "Could it be her?"

Joe sank into himself with this description.

"Yeah," he said slowly. "Yeah. Could be." He blinked to erase the dread of his imaginings beyond the other side of the wall.

The man softened and took Joe's elbow and led him forward, finding a space directly along the yellow tape. Others stepped back providing room for them, respecting the taller man.

"Officer," the man said, "this guy might know something." The cop didn't acknowledge him. "He thinks it might be his wife."

The deputy's eyes flitted toward the pair, curious, then returned to neutral.

After trying twice more to engage the policeman, the man turned to Joe. "I'm sorry. He's not going to do nothing. It's not his job." For a few moments, Joe and the man stood regarding the back of the clapboard house, paint peeling, weeds at the bottom seams. "He's not going to stick his neck out. They never do. Not for us."

The wind picked up, portending rain. Joe held out his hand to the man.

"Thanks anyway," Joe said.

"I have to get to work," the man said, returning the gesture. He placed his other hand on Joe's shoulder. "Good luck, brother."

Joe nodded and turned to face the thin blue line again.

"Hey, excuse me," Joe said. Then getting vociferous, "Can you tell me who they found? Is that my wife in there? Is it her?"

He continued to yell, getting hoarse with the effort.

While Joe stood outside the house, I worked inside unaware of his shouting. I knelt in a cramped stairwell, barely enough room for the lead detective, the dead body, and me. Darkness encircled us except for one tactical flashlight. Electrical power had long ago been cut off to this abandoned building.

Mike, the detective, and I had worked together on other homicides. He wasn't my first choice for a partner. Being just a few years from retirement, he disliked non-straightforward cases. The unknown tired him.

"Here, Doc," he said, focusing the beam on the woman's face.

She appeared my age, early forties but she could have been younger; a hard life and death age a person. She had a similar petite build, but her jawline was strong, nose delicate, lips full. Curly black hair styled in a high fade graced her head: stunning, *Vogue* worthy.

Trauma eroded some of her finer features. Eyes bulged with the lids drawn back. Tributaries of blood vessels dotted the sclerae. Her lower lip puffed out, crusted with dried blood. A tan smear stained her cheek and jaw with an aroma of vomit. Bruises and scratches flecked the sides of her neck melding into brown skin. Her face was slightly wasted. Anorexia? Drug use? Postmortem change?

Balancing on a step above the body, I shone my Maglite along the rest of her silhouette—supine on the bottom landing, the top of her head rested against the outside door. She was a naked figure except for white ankle-length socks that covered her feet.

Her arms lay at her sides, hands resting beneath her thighs. Contusions bloomed on her thorax and shoulders and encircled her wrists. Legs were drawn up and out as if awaiting a gynecologist's exam. One knee propped against a wall, the other dropped all the way to the floor. The pubic hair, shaved recently, showed uneven re-growth. Examining her pelvic region, I noted rips and bleeding in the vagina.

A rancid odor permeated the small space; used condoms strewn the floor. I counted thirteen, then re-counted the same—thirteen, an unlucky number. They were too desiccated to yield DNA from the night of her murder though we sent them to the lab anyway.

"Let's roll her," I said. My voice echoed in the shaft. "I need to see her back."

Mike and I moved her easily. Rigor mortis, a stiffening of the muscles after death, had already come and gone.

Extensive abrasions covered her posterior, concentrated along the spine, lower ribs, and buttocks from friction with the hard surface beneath her. Beer caps, soda tops, edges of candy wrappers, and empty dime bags stuck to her skin. Mouse droppings and crusted dirt layered beneath her. Scarves of dust rested in the corners.

Experience told me she had been raped and strangled here, then abandoned, more than 36 hours ago by the look of it.

"We'll need a full sexual-assault kit," I said. "Let's start with the hands. Then run the fingerprints right away."

Mike grunted. "Can't it wait until the morgue?"

"We need to get an ID on her as soon as we can," I said, explaining my request to alleviate his reluctance.

"Well, I'll have to get the evidence kit from the car." He didn't move.

This woman was a Jane Doe. The place unoccupied. The white socks her only clothing. No purse. No jewelry. Surgical scars and tattoos not visible. No obvious dental work. None of the usual hints to an identity.

The police had checked their local database for any adult black female reported missing in the past 72 hours in Central New York. I knew she hadn't been here longer than that. The fingerprints would be crucial if she had any on file.

With a huff, Mike acquiesced.

"Yeah, she'll have something on file," he said. "Another dead hooker."

His callousness irritated me. My jaw clenched. A rapping from the outside interrupted my response.

"Yeah?" Mike called out.

The officer on the other side replied, "Quite a gathering, sir."
"How many?"
"Twenty. Twenty-five."
Mike sighed. "We got to move this along, Doc."
"Then get me the fucking kit," I said.

After an hour of photographing, collecting trace evidence, and labeling each container, we laid the woman into a body bag and sealed it closed. The next part of the examination would be done at the morgue. A long day awaited me; a homicide autopsy could take eight hours.

The back door was just inches from where we were standing. If we took the woman out that way, the neighbors would see. By now, reporters were probably there too. Instead, transport services picked up the body bag, headed up the stairs and then back down to the main door at the front of the house, a more circuitous but less visible route. I left Mike to carry all the evidence we collected.

Going to my car, parked beyond the crowd, I heard a man shouting. The solo patrolman yelled in return. I moved closer to listen.

"Is it my wife? Is it her?" the man croaked. He paced in front of the bystanders who had given him a wide berth. The harried deputy strove to keep order.

"I asked you to step back, sir," the officer said as the man leaned into the crime scene tape.

"Damn it. What's going on? Is it her? Is it Lashana?"

My world intersected with Joe's.

I approached the policeman and read his nameplate.

"Deputy Stanton," I said. He flashed irritation before noticing the forensic badge I held toward him. "What's going on here?"

"Not a problem, ma'am," the officer said, color rising in his face. "This gentleman insists on going inside. Says his wife is in there. I told him this is a crime scene. Police are investigating. He won't listen. I'm about to call for backup." He had one hand on his radio.

"I don't think that's necessary, Deputy," I said. I turned to the man who had gone quiet during the conversation. "What is your name, sir?"

"Joe," he said, "Joe Warren."

"Officer, call Detective Faster and maybe we can sort this out."

The officer radioed Mike my request.

Extending my hand, I introduced myself to Joe.

He seemed confused by this civility after being ignored for so long. He grasped my hand in both of his. Strong, callused, and trembling, he shook mine. Taking in my white lab coat, he paled, aware of what my title might signify.

Mike emerged from around the corner at a hurried pace.

"Yeah, Doc?" he said, breathing hard. He had taken the same precaution in exiting the walk-up, using the two flights of stairs. Perspiration trickled down the sides of his face.

"This man might have some information for us, Detective," I said, guiding Joe toward a neighboring structure, a rotting porch with trash piled in a corner, yet private.

"Sir, can you show me some ID please," Mike asked, retrieving a pen and notepad from his suit jacket.

Joe patted his t-shirt and athletic pants before realizing there were no pockets.

"Wait a minute," Joe said and ran back to his residence.

"What's his deal?" Mike said to me.

"He thinks the woman in there might be his wife," I said. Mike raised his eyebrows.

Joe wheezed a little when he returned and showed his driver's license to Mike. The investigator dutifully noted the information.

Mike interviewed Joe, and I interjected from time to time. The detective's style was to ask open-ended questions. Joe's answers rambled, touching upon the distant past then skipping into the future. The only knowable present was his being here. His wife's absence was impenetrable. Mike worked on getting a coherent statement.

Joe ran his hands over his shirt as if to find a packet of cigarettes.

"We should quit anyway. I been telling her that," Joe said. He lapsed to the recurrent, "Is it her? Is it my wife?"

"Information you give us will help sort this out," I said, feeling sorrow for his anguished refrain.

"We were gonna go to the farmer's market on Saturday."

Rain drizzled as we huddled under the portico overhang. The crowd dissipated as if sensing the victim's departure. Mike and I waited to hear something about recent days. Joe shuddered in his thin clothing.

"I've been worried about her," he said. "She's been going out, not saying where." He shook his head. "I didn't know what to do. She'd just up and get mad at me for no reason." He didn't want to believe that she had slipped back into drugs, the familiar pulling her in like old sneakers sucked into fresh mud.

My pager and Mike's radio sounded at the same time. We excused ourselves and walked out of earshot. Mike scribbled a note. I read the message on my screen. They said the same thing—Fingerprint identification is a match. The murdered woman was Lashana Warren. The CODIS state-wide fingerprint system had connected the dead woman with an arrest report from eight years ago.

I sagged with the official news.

Mike had more data from her rap sheet. It revealed a turbulent decade in her twenties—cocaine and marijuana use/possession, and solicitation —a vulnerable woman on the edge of society.

Joe had told us that his wife had turned her life around. He was well-acquainted with her past; he had one of his own. They both had been clean for years, throughout their marriage and more, but not today. The rapid drug test on Lashana's nasal swab was positive for cocaine.

As we returned, he looked expectantly at us. The bad news had to wait a few minutes.

"When did you last see Lashana, Mr. Warren?" Mike said. The hardest part for any next-of-kin, describing their final moment with the deceased.

Joe swallowed and his voice cracked.

"When she went out night before last," he said. "No, wait. The night before that. What was that, Monday?"

"Today is Wednesday," I said.

"Oh," Joe said, "I've been looking for her for two nights. Sunday, then. Yeah, it was Sunday night. The last time I went to work. She went out for smokes. She likes Kools, not my Camels. Says they're too harsh." He spoke quickly.

"What time was that?" Mike asked, continuing to take notes.

"Maybe 9 or 10 o'clock," Joe said. "That corner store is open to eleven. I had to head to work, and she wasn't back yet. Around midnight I called her but got no answer. When I came home the next morning, she wasn't there. Something felt wrong. She never stays out all night. I thought maybe she slept over her mom's, so I called Nelly and...." He let the end of the sentence trail off.

"Did she say anything else when she left?" Mike said.

Joe didn't answer, lost in memories of that conversation.

"I don't know what all I said. Maybe I said, 'Don't bang the door' or 'I'm headed to the job soon' or 'Be careful.' I've been thinking about this all the time." His breath hitched, "Yeah, that sounds right. 'Be careful.'" He nodded, inhaling deeply then coughing for several seconds. "Sorry about that. We both need to stop smoking." Then tearfully, "Maybe I said that already."

Joe pressed on.

"I don't think I said, 'I love you.' I didn't say it. How awful is that? I didn't say 'I love you, baby.' I didn't say it," Joe's body shook. His eyes widened. "Why did she lie? Why? I would have helped her. I always did." He began to sob. "I love you, baby. Why did you go?"

"Joe," I said touching his arm, "do you know what happened?"

"No, I don't, but people are saying all kinds of shit. They're saying there's a woman killed, maybe on drugs. Someone saw the hearse out front. You're the medical examiner, right? That's like a coroner, isn't it? You only come out when they're dead." His eyes were swollen, pupils dilated with anxiety, nose running. He asked the questions he had been repeating for hours, "Is it her? Is it my wife?"

The skies wept around us.

"It is, Mr. Warren," I said, "Your wife is dead." His arm felt cold. Joe wobbled a step back. Mike stood close.

"The fingerprints of the woman we found match Lashana Warren," Mike said.

"I'm sorry for your loss," I said, immediately hating the sound of my words, a worthless platitude as if someone had misplaced their car keys. Any further condolence became lost to his wails of misery. He had known yet didn't want to believe; the nightmare realized. My inadequate apology caked my tongue to the roof of my mouth.

"Are you sure it's her?" he said.

Thoughts of my husband, my love, lying alone, deserted, unnamed, brought tears to my eyes. How would I go on? Could I go on? What if I never held him again? Had I said 'I love you' this morning?

"It is her, Mr. Warren," I said simply.

He keened again as if hearing about her death for the first time. It bit into me.

"How did she die? Was it the blow?" he asked, staccato words between breaths. He turned to the detective for an answer.

"That's what we're trying to find out," Mike said. He shifted back and forth, looking down at his feet.

"There are a lot of things that need to be done before we have any answers," I said. "I am going to do an autopsy and there will be specialized exams—x-rays, drug testing, lab work. This is an active investigation, so I won't be able to give you all the details right away. Do you understand?"

"What do you mean by that? Didn't she OD?" Joe asked.

Mike gave the smallest of nods for me to continue. Joe deserved something more. I couldn't give him much.

"It's more complicated than that," I said.

"What are you talking about? Did she fall? She didn't kill herself, did she? Did somebody do something to her?" With each question, Joe's confusion ratcheted higher. The enormity of what I couldn't say lodged in my throat.

"We have to do this methodically and carefully—no premature judgments. We want the truth. We have to do this right for Lashana," I said.

He nodded but didn't understand. "But, please, tell me how she died. Was she killed?"

Did what he imagined even come close to the violence in the stairwell?

"As soon as I can, I will tell you." I offered the same explanation to Joe's repeated questions. The grief-stricken often became temporarily deaf.

"I've been trying to find her for two days and she was right here." He stamped his foot. "What the hell? Why would she go here?" He stared at the scuffed door which bewildered him as much as whatever his wife had done. "What is this place? Some crack house?"

"We're looking into that and the doctor here is going to take care of Lashana," Mike said.

"You have to go with the police now to answer some questions," I said, grateful to the detective for his newfound sensitivity. Alarm registered on Joe's face.

"Do you think I did something to her? I didn't do nothing. I kept her safe, away from all that crap." Anger surfaced along with the guilt of failing to protect her. "I would never hurt her. How could I? You should be ashamed. I been out here yelling for hours." Joe had described all of it to us—the agony of shouting into the void. "I didn't know where she was." With this last proclamation, he deflated—shoulders slumped, head bowed. Maybe he figured he should have known where she was after all.

"Yeah, yeah," Joe said, though he was shaking his head back and forth as if he didn't believe what he was saying. "I understand. You just want to know what happened." He sniffed then added, "I do, too."

"Let's get you someplace warm," Mike said. Lashana's husband went willingly to the unmarked car and straightened as they walked.

He and Mike headed to the station and then the morgue. Joe wanted to make a visual identification of his wife. We already had a scientific ID. After looking for days and waiting outside the building for hours, maybe he needed to see Lashana in the flesh to make the death real.

Joe underwent routine questioning. As the significant other and the last person known to see the victim alive, he was the usual suspect. It wasn't my job to solve the whodunit. Yet I knew he hadn't killed her—this heinous act of strangulation and rape. His palpable sorrow exonerated him in my mind. Quickly the police came to the same conclusion after their official interview.

After leaving the scene, I started my car.

On the radio, a newscaster announced, "The body of a woman was found early this morning in the city in an abandoned building known for illegal drug activity. The site has also been used for prostitution. She died from an apparent drug overdose."

No official conclusion had been released from my office. Did the reporter get his information from the police or the neighborhood gawkers? Lashana was brutally murdered and all he had to say was that she's a druggie and a whore? That should have been a harbinger of the disappointment that was to come at the trial.

Ultimately, a perpetrator was arrested, the last john to have been with her. He admitted to seeing Lashana in the same position as we had seen her in the stairwell. He described her body exactly as he left her, which was exactly as we found her. Things got rough during sex; he put his hands around her throat. She passed out. He walked away.

At the trial, I testified that Lashana was killed by manual strangulation —someone fatally choked her. The drugs in her blood were at low levels, not a cause of her demise. No viable DNA was recovered from her body. Any sperm in the condoms had degraded. She had spent nearly three days in the stairwell, enough time for biologic material to decay.

The jury's verdict was "Not Guilty." There were no fibers, blood, or fingerprints on the body to connect the defendant to the scene despite his confession. The lack of semen was more important to the jurors than the defendant's admission that he had killed her.

In forensic pathology, we call this the "CSI Effect": the expectation that there will be physical evidence present each and every time a crime is committed. To a group of one's peers charged with assessing guilt or innocence, the evidence matters more than witness statements, motive, means, opportunity, or even confessions. But on that Wednesday, these court events were months into the future. I hadn't even signed the death certificate yet.

My last glimpse of Joe was of him sitting in the backseat of the police cruiser, head on his knees. His wife had died just across from where they lived; yards from the spot where he had been worrying for two days and nights. It would be many weeks before he learned the depressing particulars and still more before justice completely slipped away.

Thunder rumbled. I flipped on the windshield wipers and headlights. The air from the defroster was cold. I raised the temperature. My stomach growled but I was not hungry. My day had started early and would go into the evening. I flipped on the voice recorder and described my findings from the scene.

Dead Lashana alternated in my mind with a gauzy imagining of her alive. Her neck with its bloody marks of pain contrasted with a tender one bent toward Joe. Naked and clothed, darkness and light, suffering and comfort. The images flicked on and off in rhythm with the wipers.

I stopped the dictation and drove to the office.

One, one thousand, two, one thousand, three, one thousand. I counted to 15 seconds with the beating of the wiper blades. The time it might take until she passed out. Glancing at the clock, I waited for time to advance five minutes. An average amount of time to deprive the brain of oxygen and snuff out her life. Had her last thought been of Joe?

Pulling my car into the parking lot of the Center for Forensic Sciences, I stared out the front window. It was raining cats and dogs. The sound of the wipers beat loud and steady. Water pooled at the edge of the windshield, pushed to the side like Lashana's naked form. It drained and reshaped with each swipe of the rubber arm. The dead woman's image held firm: head against the door, arms to the side, legs splayed, and wearing only socks.

A question gathered from the wet hallucination; one that congealed over the days, weeks, and months to come.

Never answered. Not satisfied. Forever lost.

Thwomp. Thwomp. Thwomp. Thwomp.

Where. Were. Her. Clothes?

Watching Her

The minivan was filled with inflatables, towels, a cooler, and three excited boys. Marc drove. We fielded the kids' repeated question of "Are we there yet?" as cars slowly approached the Sagamore Bridge. My family and I were headed to Cape Cod, our annual summer sojourn. It was 2003.

The FM dial stayed tuned to 102, a classic rock station. The song began with drums, double bass, and acoustic guitar. Gordon Sumner's tenor joined at the 15-second mark. The middle tom-tom and snare alternated beats with an upright bass throbbing a double count. "Every Breath You Take," a huge hit for The Police, won Best Song at the 1983 Grammys. Even 20 years later, the radio played Sting's familiar melody a lot.

Words sung from a shattered heart—breath, move, bond, step, vow, smile, claim. A strong desire for possession felt in the aftermath of separation. The lyrics undid me.

In the front passenger seat, I turned toward the window and closed my eyes, unable to avoid the images of the murdered woman from a different hot summer day.

In the humid morgue, the plastic protective gear had felt suffocating. I wore an N-95 mask, face shield, plastic gown, booties, and a double layer of gloves. The schedule was busy that day with three cases in the morning. All of them required full autopsy examinations.

The first woman lay on the gurney, bloody from the knife attack. Stabs and slices concentrated on her head, neck, and upper chest surrounded by cerise smears. The loss of blood paled her naturally brown skin. Her eyes were wide open. I closed her eyelids.

I counted 103 sharp wounds on her body. Superficial cuts lined her hands and forearms where she had tried to cover her head. The yellow underpinning of the fatty tissue of her scalp glistened from slashes down to the skull. Black hair matted in the wounds. Dozens of bruises colored her arms and legs from the struggle with her killer.

A trail of open lesions began on her face in front of the right ear and extended to the shoulder. The blade was thrust and removed in a staccato fashion. Each injury by itself might have been survivable. Except for one, right below the middle of the collarbone; the underlying artery severed by the puncture. If someone had been able to get close enough to apply pressure, maybe she wouldn't have lost a fatal amount of blood.

The scene had been horrific. Dried and liquid red gore surrounded the woman as she sprawled on the floor, the air redolent with freshly spilled blood. The original white of her uniform was dyed crimson with it. Chaotic scarlet footprints patterned the ground. The six-inch-long murder weapon lay across the room like a weapon discarded in battle.

Her ex-husband had been stalking her for weeks. Hours before her death, he phoned and threatened her. She had an order of protection, but the cops told her that the man wasn't physically near her, so they were powerless to react to verbal intimidation.

The woman worked in a nursing home. Her former spouse watched from the street for a few minutes. Then he pushed past the receptionist, assistants, and patients. In a communal room, he grabbed her from behind. She was a big woman, but no match for his more muscular frame and adrenaline-fueled passion. Screaming, kicking, punching, she fought him. Co-workers threw furniture at him as he continued to stab her with a butcher knife. One chair broke as it hit his back. An attendant tried to grasp the man's pant legs. The attacker swung the blade in a wide arc preventing anyone from drawing near.

A clerk dialed 9-1-1.

Photos and affidavits documented this. I had listened to the recording, the air filled with wails and sobs.

In the morgue, it was quiet except for the radio.

"And now, an oldie but a goodie from Sting and one of the top 100 songs of the twentieth century," said the DJ.

Her ex-lover was watching her, and then I was.

TSUNAMI

THE helicopter flew through the clear blue sky, the sun low on the horizon. The pilot talked to us through the headset, advising of position and geography. An anthropologist and I were headed to the island of Phi Phi off the southwestern coast of Thailand. Large rock formations jutted out of the water, beckoning adventurous climbers. We identified our target by the billowing smoke arising from the land.

The Andaman Sea calmly lapped at the shore as we touched down on the sand. It had been three weeks since an earthquake and tsunami had hit the Indian Ocean during the winter holiday of 2004.

The blades stopped whirring and we stepped out.

Derek and I were part of the contingent representing the USA for the Thailand Tsunami Victim Identification project, an international response of 39 countries to help put names to the victims. Over 8,000 people were dead or missing, 2,000 were tourists. At that point, 300 Americans were unaccounted for.

Brrring. Brrring. Brrring.

Less than a week earlier, my home telephone rang on a Sunday night.

Joshua, a sophomore in high school, had answered. A colleague, Elias, who I worked with at Ground Zero, was calling from Asia. As Joshua handed me the receiver he started crying. My family was hyper-aware of the meaning of evening phone calls asking for Dr. J and bringing death in one form or another that took me away from home for as much as a month at a time.

When I hung up the phone, Joshua said, "How long?"

I crossed the room. My tall man/boy hugged me, and I leaned into him.

"At least two weeks," I said. That was the typical federal deployment schedule.

"Be careful," he said. "I love you."

I went to tell the rest of the family.

On Phi Phi, Derek and I walked toward the center portion of the isthmus. The island had been completely drenched from both sides covering the town in the center, destroying most of its buildings which sat only six feet above sea level.

"Whoa," Derek said. "Watch out for the rubble."

Assigned as my deputy, he felt responsible to keep me safe. We hadn't worked together before but through a complicated amalgam of the Department of Homeland Security, the US State Department, Health and Human Services, and the Joint POW/MIA Accounting Command, we became partners. In his normal nine-to-five life, he was a PhD in anthropology, spending his days in the laboratory in Honolulu identifying human remains mostly belonging to US soldiers from the Vietnam war era. His specialty was bones, mine was soft tissue. We made a great team.

Grasses, bamboo, rope, and wood littered the area. Palm trees were downed. Fronds scattered around them like discarded branches from a Holy Week celebration. We stepped around jagged sheets of blue aluminum as we crossed the beach. As my eyes adjusted to the sun, I saw the edge of a passport peeking out of the sand. I opened it to see a woman's face who looked eerily like me. The front cover had the stamp of the country, Sweden, *Sverige*.

"We should collect any personal items before they get burned," I said.

"I agree," Derek said as he picked up a leather wallet, water damaged but with legible identification. "They seem eager to burn all the refuse."

"Everything's destroyed. Who knows how long it will take authorities to get here from the mainland to help them deal with this. There's enough going on in Phuket and Krabi." I referred to the temporary morgues set up in those towns handling hundreds of dead each day.

"Yeah, two hours by boat and how many of those boats are still functioning."

Trash burned in piles around us as the survivors dealt with the wreckage from the disaster. Prior to the tsunami, this island had been a haven, part of a marine park, catering to SCUBA divers and snorkelers. Since *The Beach* was filmed on location here in 2000, each year brought increased numbers of tourists.

Dive charts and mangled signs scattered the area, the red and white in stark contrast to the beige, green colors of nature. A tropical bar had caved in on itself. As we got closer, the odor of decomposition assailed us, rancid and distinct from the smoke.

"There are still bodies here," I said.

"Yeah, and in the ponds around, too," Derek said. "That backhoe should be careful."

We watched as a machine scraped the ground, collecting debris and putting it in a pile to be burned. In forensics, excavations were careful with a lot of manual shoveling to avoid damaging the bodies. Backhoes were used sparingly. I looked at Derek and raised my eyebrows, wondering if he was thinking the same.

"Hang on, that police officer looks in charge, I'll give him a heads up," Derek said.

It felt like a noble, futile act. The dead were everywhere, not just on Phi Phi but washed up on the shore of the mainland and carried miles to the interior by the 30-foot-high waves. Some people had been on beaches and verandas mesmerized as the water receded before the sea lashed back and swallowed them. Others were trapped in boats and cars, tossed about in a violent swirl. Many were caught in a current of steel detritus and cement; buildings torn apart as if King Kong had rampaged through the coast.

At least three mobile morgues were set up on the mainland to help identify the dead. We were scheduled to visit each and report back. There were thousands dead and missing. How could we attend to the smell of a few decomposing bodies?

Besides, most Thai cremate their dead. In accordance with Buddhist tradition, this is done close to where their loved one died to keep the spirit from wandering far. Yet, the temperature of this trash fire would never be high enough to effectively burn a corpse.

Derek jogged back.

"He's aware," he said.

We walked from one side of the island to the other, treading carefully, methodically. We paused to make notes about the devastation. Some Americans had been vacationing here. The embassy was still trying to contact the families of the missing travelers. We collected more papers for identification. The smell of raw sewage wrapped around us.

The sun reached its zenith. During our walk-about, the temperature had risen above 90 degrees. My shirt clung to me. My cargo pants chafed. An occasional gust of sea wind brought misty relief.

The pilot signaled to us. He had other missions that day. We did too.

"Let's go," I said. "We can get this material back to the appropriate countries." The representatives would be at the executive committee meeting that afternoon.

We returned to the helicopter, carrying the smell of burning trash with us and our paper bag of IDs.

The chopper ascended. The island and smoke disappeared. Tranquil sea and green island hills filled the vista.

The natural beauty reminded me of a trip 20 years earlier, to Bangkok, Chiang Mai, and Hua Hin; Marc and I on an engagement vacation, purchased instead of a ring. We bought Thai silk and had my wedding gown made at the Jim Thompson House. The women seamstresses smiled, laughed, and fussed about me, measuring every inch of my torso and arms. I felt like a princess. Cherishing that dress, I had it shortened and wore it for our tenth anniversary, celebrated at the Rainbow Room in NYC. It hangs in my closet still, though the white has yellowed with the passing of time.

The rhythmic spinning of the blades merged into the sweet tones of Thai: *khàawp-khun khâ* and *khàawp-khun khrâp*. The words mean thank you. I don't remember how long it took to get back to our station in Phuket.

It took me much longer to get back to my life in Syracuse when I left Thailand three weeks later.

AUTHORITY

INDUSTRIAL fans hummed loudly throughout the warehouse. My skin itched in the heavy plastic gown; the heat was insufferable. My breath escaped above the surgical mask, fogging my glasses. I had forgotten to tape the gap over my nose. Sweat trickled beneath my hair bonnet. I had to pee.

"Is there a bathroom closer than the admin office?" I asked my assistant, Dennis.

"Well," he paused, "you can go through that door behind x-ray. There's a patch of lawn. It's private."

The guys must have known about this all week.

My choices were to remove all my PPE, walk two blocks back and forth to the toilet, redress in full protective gear OR lift gown, drop pants, pee on the grass. Not ideal, but very little was in a natural disaster.

The relief was instantaneous. The scene could have been from a hiking trip in the Adirondacks except for the surrounding cement walls and lack of foliage. The smell of urine permeated, but less perceptibly than the aroma of decay from the morgue.

There, at least twice an hour, a body greeted me, victims of Hurricane Katrina. Recovered from rooftops and attics, bights and basins, they were brought in and doused with chlorine in a crude attempt at bacterial decontamination.

As New Orleans had plunged underwater, the dead were tethered to lamp posts and telephone poles to keep them from floating away. People died in their houses, in hospitals, nursing homes, and the Superdome.

They died rapidly from drowning or slowly from wounds and infection due to the dirty water. None of the decedents were recovered quickly.

The smell was nauseating—a mixture of decomposition, mildew, sewage, and disinfectant. My limbic system acknowledged it and then tucked it away. Even the grotesque visual scene—swollen torsos, slipping skin, unrecognizable faces, green discoloration—were familiar to me. These were my patients. I worked to return their identities.

Dennis approached and handed me a file; he was a forensic anthropologist in his life outside DMORT. Here he functioned as a pathology assistant. The records revealed that this person already had a name. He pulled the gurney up to the autopsy station with instruments prepped.

A cachectic woman, weighing barely 100 pounds, lay face up on the steel table. Three different color bands encircled her wrists. I bent closer to read the imprints: her name, a Do Not Resuscitate (DNR) order, and an active tuberculosis warning. Instead of being overwhelmed by the infection that was eating away her lungs, the tempest waters suffocated her.

"Let me go talk to the coroner," I said. "Take five." I ended up taking off my PPE anyway.

The sunny outside, a sharp contrast to the artificial indoor lighting, made my eyes water. The metal door clanged as I entered the trailer. The coroner sat alone in the office. The man was a local fixture having already served more than three decades in power. He was a physician, like me, but unlike me, he had no formal forensic training. In his position, he oversaw this whole operation: made decisions on who needed autopsies, approved postmortem identifications, and signed death certificates. The federal team was here to assist him.

The air-conditioned office chilled me. Sitting behind the desk, he held up an index finger and continued to review a page in a file. Seconds passed feeling like minutes. I had been in continuous motion since arriving here, called to serve by my country. This was my sixth mass disaster response in 8 years. He finally looked up.

"Mary, what can I do for you?" His tone was smooth.

"We just received a case of active tuberculosis and it's marked for autopsy," I said. "Maybe it was miscoded?"

He took the file I handed him, spending less time with it than he had made me wait. He gave it back.

"No," he said. "There's no mistake."

I considered the ramifications. We worked in a building never meant to be a morgue, with inadequate ventilation and no filters to take airborne pathogens away or ultraviolet lights to kill viruses or bacteria. Fans blew germs around the room. We had only surgical masks, not the specialized N-95s to protect us. He knew all of this.

"I recommend we limit it to an external examination, x-rays, and review the medical records instead of cutting the body open. Sir, we know why she died. The wing of the hospital was flooded."

"Every single person that died in any chronic care facility gets an autopsy. End of story. Lord knows there will be lawsuits aplenty with this."

"Normally, I would agree, but this is too great a risk to the 100 people working in the morgue, all of whom would be exposed. We are not equipped to handle this pathogen."

He stared at me, and I at him.

I told him about a historic outbreak in my hometown where clerical workers tested positive for TB after tuberculous prisoners were autopsied several rooms away. Sawing open bone dispersed the tiny germs into the atmosphere and people breathed them in. That morgue also had deficits of ventilation. I reminded him how hardy this tiny germ was, found in skeletons thousands of years old.

He came from behind his desk and placed a hand on my shoulder, saying "Now, honey, we don't worry about TB in these parts."

I thought of Aldous Huxley—"Facts do not cease to exist because they are ignored."

"My team will not be doing this case," I said, and left.

I stepped out into the sunlight. The muscles of my upper back tightened—sore from hunching over the gurneys all morning and the added burden of the conversation with the coroner. I reached my arms overhead for a long stretch.

The sky was cloudless, the air humid, warmer than the trailer, cooler than the morgue. I needed a moment to formulate the unexpected plan B. Naively, I had assumed the experienced surgeon would agree with me; any physician should have agreed with me.

At the morgue, I replaced my hair bonnet, protective glasses, surgical mask, gown, booties, and gloves. I stood on a folding chair. Silence settled over the group.

"Listen up," I said. "Thanks everyone for working so hard. This announcement is for my federal team, DMORT. We are evacuating the morgue due to a case of active tuberculosis. You might already know that this can be spread in the air even postmortem. It's especially dangerous if bone saws are used. The local authorities are ordering an autopsy on this patient. So, everybody on my team will leave the building and not return for four hours. This allows one hour for the autopsy, two hours to let the airborne pathogens settle, and one for a buffer. Let's pull out now."

I stepped down. No one questioned my decision.

As my team filed out the door, Dennis asked, "Why would he do that?"

I sighed, shaking my head. "Because he can."

The Champion

The bedside clock read 6 a.m.

"Mom, I forgot one of my wrestling shoes," Joshua said.

I groaned into the phone's handset and pondered how he could have only one shoe.

"I'm sorry. Chris picked me up early and I think I left it in my car."

His trunk was messy. The trip had started before dawn.

"Okay, okay," I said, wiping the sleep from my eyes and resigned to the early Saturday awakening. "What time does your match start?"

"Eight. But Coach says I need it now. To warm up and stuff."

"Alright, let me grab a cup of coffee and I'll head out. I love you."

"Me too. Thanks a lot."

The day had been upended like a surprise pin in a match.

Marc was supposed to watch the morning events as Joshua competed in an invitational high school tournament, the last big event of his senior year. I would have come later in the afternoon. The missing shoe required my expertise. I'm the family sleuth for lost things. My photographic visual memory along with my professional detective skills make me the go-to person when someone can't find a needed item.

I drove to the college 30 minutes from home with the shoe. After successfully delivering the forgotten gear, I sat in the upper bleachers to watch the matches.

Twelve hours later, the air was heavy in the gymnasium, and I fanned myself with the program. Trickles of moisture ran down my neck. March in Central New York remained winter, but the arena full of testosterone felt tropical. My butt had long ago gone numb from sitting on a flat metal bench. I had only gotten up a few times for a bathroom break and to get a Snickers bar from the vending machine, afraid to miss my son's matches. I was his only supporter here—Marc had gone with the other brothers to their sporting competitions.

Joshua had won four already, advancing him far in the tournament.

The announcer said my son's name over the crackling loudspeaker. I scanned the room and saw Joshua striding onto one of a dozen 20-by-20-foot black mats. I hadn't talked to him all day as he competed. As a senior, his wrestling career was about to end with this last match.

As each of my sons had entered junior high, I required them to pick a sport, any sport they wanted. Marc oversaw their musical careers; I was responsible for the athletics. Marty chose basketball—he had been playing since the age of five and trying to handle the ball since three. Though the shortest of the family, he loved it with a passion, becoming an excellent three-point shooter, and defensive player. When he got older, he expressed disappointment that he stood well below his two older brothers.

"If I were taller, I'd be an awesome basketball player," Marty said.

"Really, you think so?" I said. "You're such a great player because you're shorter. You've had to work really hard to go up against guys a head taller than you. You're fast and accurate." He grinned.

David chose a different sport every year, which suited his mercurial character. He was tall enough for volleyball, strong enough for rowing, fast enough for cross-country. He relished sliding in the mud in football and leaping for the long jump in track and field. He enjoyed the team camaraderie; he didn't have a favorite sport.

Joshua chose wrestling.

The first match he invited me to before joining the team heightened my maternal sensibilities. I watched boys smacking the mats, grunting, and struggling for a hand or foot hold to stay in the game. An individual competition had three two-minute rounds. Afterwards, limbs quivered, legs wobbled, and sometimes kids threw up. Six minutes in wrestling was a marathon.

Throughout middle school and high school, I watched Joshua compete. I saw the adrenaline rush, the raw physical exertion, and ultimate exhaustion at the end of the meet. Wrestling was a personally demanding endeavor, physically and emotionally.

Was he up to this final challenge?

At six feet, Joshua was muscular in his 187-pound weight class. Clumps of curly brown hair sprouted from his head; the length just short enough to forgo a cap. The ear protectors with the chin strap looked inadequate to prevent serious injury. He wore the traditional onesie, a tank top and boxer briefs combination, appearing like a mod Fred Flintstone.

He looked steady facing his opponent yet exuded an air of teen vulnerability. Shouts from other contestants, whistles, and cheers sounded in the background. The referee raised and dropped his arm signaling go.

The two boys circled each other like boxers, making grabs with their hands. Joshua bounced lightly on his feet, back and forth, never losing the focus of his opponent's eyes. He lunged and made slapping contact with the boy. They fell like drunken dancers taking a tumble. An *oof* emitted from their entangled mass as they smacked hard on the vinyl mat.

They rolled, arms out, legs akimbo, a whirling blur of red and green, blonde and brunette, careening from side to side on the floor. It wasn't clear who had the advantage. I stood up. My heart pounded.

"Go Josh," I shouted, my voice tinny, lost in the vast space.

On the ground, the battle became all-out muscle clenching as they balanced on their sides. Joshua's head and shoulders struggled against the other boy's thighs attempting to flip my son onto his back. One strong move either way might win the contest. I watched as arms trembled and feet flexed but no one changed position. Seconds ticked on.

Each boy grappled to gain control of the match. The audience gasped as my son suddenly bulldozed his opponent. The other boy arched his back and lifted one shoulder off the mat awkwardly, trying to avoid being pinned, which would mean an immediate loss.

The referee got down, crawling around the pair of fighters with his ear to the ground as if listening for a herd of buffalo in the distance, carefully observing whether the opponent's shoulders touched the ground. I waited for the ref to smack the mat signaling the pin. Instead, all three figures suddenly sprang to their feet. The boys circled again in a primitive ritual of aggression.

Joshua dove gracefully forward into his opponent's midsection and tossed the teen over his hip. This dramatic move sent the boy arcing over my son's body, and onto the floor landing with a loud *thwack*. Both of the boy's shoulders had made contact.

My son jumped up and pumped both fists downward as he paced, feeling the rush of victory. The referee grabbed Joshua's right hand and held it up in the air, the sign of the winner.

Joshua looked to the bleachers and saw me cheering. An intense energy passed between us.

"I did it," his eyes telegraphed.

"I know, I was here with you," mine replied.

We might have been the only two people in the room; that moment lasted a long time.

Not only did Joshua win his weight class division that day but also the wrestling equivalent of Most Valuable Player for the tournament. He received two statuette trophies and a long sleeve tee-shirt with the word *CHAMPION* printed down one sleeve.

After many seasons of this difficult sport, times of failure and disappointment, weight disqualifications, clementine orange diets, and long drives around Central New York to competitions, he won this crowning achievement in his senior year and had a 17-3 record.

Nearly seven months later, in his first semester of college, Joshua faced a larger battle. It had begun with a malaise that felt like the flu. Then his legs got progressively weaker. I drove to pick him up from college. He needed some chicken soup and rest, things not available at the university.

I went into his bedroom at home the next morning with a cup of tea and a piece of toast.

"Mom, my hand feels weird," Joshua said.

"Squeeze mine," I said, my physician diagnostics at work. His grip was weak, very weak.

I diagnosed ascending paralysis—starting in his lower limbs and progressing to his upper—the hallmark of Guillain-Barré syndrome. This fight was inside his body.

"We're going to go to the hospital for a few tests," I said, steadying my breathing and my words.

I helped him dress and he leaned on me as we hobbled to the car.

"What's the worst that can happen, Mom?" His voice was calm.

I paused. My kids have told me that sometimes I'm too honest.

"You could stop breathing."

"I could die?"

That question hung heavy in the air between us. I willed myself not to cry, to stay strong for my son. I reached over and buckled his seatbelt. His breath had quickened, as if proving that he could still do this simple act.

"We need to head straight to the ER. They have ventilators there. I'm with you now," I said, hoping the facts provided reassurance.

When we arrived at the emergency room, he was hours away from needing a respirator. His blood had made antibodies against his nerves, affecting most of his body—swallowing, heart rate, blood pressure, and skeletal muscles. Paralysis overtook him up to his chest.

Treatment came swiftly. Tubes and lines and protective wrappings made their way along his skin. Medications infused into his veins. Machines beeped to alert the nurses of changes in his respiratory or cardiac status. The staff rolled him at regular intervals. He couldn't move on his own.

He required immunoglobulin therapy and multiple rounds of plasmapheresis, a lengthy procedure like renal dialysis, that removed the harmful antibodies. My husband and I took turns spending the night in his room when he was in the ICU. He stayed in the hospital for six weeks.

All the years of wrestling had trained him for this battle: giving one more push in that two-minute round, losing, learning, finding inner strength despite bone-weariness, going out to the mat again and again. He gave it all he had.

A poster, pre-dating the illness, hung in my son's bedroom with the eloquent words of Theodore Roosevelt:

> "The credit belongs to the man who is actually in the arena, whose face is marred by dust and sweat and blood, who strives valiantly, who errs and comes short again and again…who at the best knows in the end the triumph of high achievement and who at the worst, if he fails, at least he fails while daring greatly, so that his place shall never be with those cold and timid souls who know neither victory nor defeat."

In the rehabilitation unit before being released from the hospital, I watched Joshua struggle along the walkway with the physical therapist at his side. A determined attitude hunched his shoulders as he held the handrails making slow forward progress. The champion shirt from his final tournament hung loose on his much thinner frame.

At the end of the ramp, I lifted one of his hands high in the air while he balanced with the other. Our eyes met in a full conversation. My son smiled and turned to take the long trek back.

The Question

The cardiac monitor sat dark and silent. A white sheet draped the young woman's lower body; wires and lines snaked out from beneath it. A pink Hello Kitty tee-shirt lay discarded on a nearby chair; cut off by emergency medical technicians who tried to restart her heart. Residue of gel from shocking paddles glistened on her chest.

Four of us (her parents and my husband and I) stood in this private room, away from the surrounding chaos of the ER. The staff had provided this seclusion; we were all physicians. I was a familiar presence investigating sudden and unexpected deaths.

Brrring. Brrring. Brrring.

Thirty minutes earlier, the girl's father, a close family friend, had called our home.

"Anna's here at the hospital. Please come," he had said.

Marc and I rushed there not knowing what awaited us.

In the sequestered area, we watched as the father, a middle-aged man, paced along one wall. Thick black hair stood in all directions on his head, as if he had run his fingers wildly through it. A misbuttoned, blue-striped shirt hung over his jeans, one tail drooping longer. Glasses sat askew on his face; bedroom slippers adorned his feet.

His partner, Anna's other father, positioned himself at the head of the stretcher. He slumped, chin to chest, his hands and forehead on the side rail. Wisps of curly black hair surrounded a central bald spot that I'd never noticed before. He startled as I touched his shoulder, then turned to grip me in a tight hug. I inhaled his familiar scent: musk and lemon.

"I'm so sorry," I said. The words sank into the hushed space. He stepped back inviting me to examine his daughter.

Remnants of mascara and copper shadow framed her brown eyes. Gently, I parted the lids revealing dilated pupils. Foamy bubbles had dried on the lips, purple compared to the pale of her cheeks. Long thick hair cascaded over her shoulders. A barcoded medical band encircled the right wrist like a bracelet from a weekend concert. Petite feet, clothed in white socks with little pom poms at the heels, peeked out at the end of the cot.

She was 21 years old, between the ages of my two older boys, men really.

A tiny dot marked the only sign of trauma, located on the side of her left forearm near the hand. The surrounding blue hue of the skin emphasized its presence with clotted blood at the center of the puncture. This site marked the fatal injection, very recent intravenous drug use. A syringe had been found next to her.

A tap on the door caught our attention. I looked at the men, who nodded simultaneously.

"Come in," I said.

A nurse in blue scrubs stepped hesitantly inside. She handed me a report with Anna's name and hospital number printed across the top. The stat laboratory results confirmed that opiates had been found.

Both fathers stared expectantly as if this paper were a reprieve—evidence that it was not their only child lying dead on the hospital bed. Perhaps this condition might miraculously be reversed.

"This is the result of the drug screen," I said. My voice sounded shriveled. "Anna died of an overdose."

A scream escaped from one father, the man who had been pacing—a sound that raised the hairs on my neck. They turned to each other in an embrace that became a rocking motion, a dance of the bereaved. Marc moved closer to me.

The parents had known about the heroin use. Anna struggled with this addiction, overdosed before, had gone to rehab, gotten clean.

Weeks later, when the quantitative toxicology testing was completed, we learned that a combination of heroin and fentanyl had killed her. Anna joined 39 others dead from the same lethal cocktail that year in the county, and more than 15,000 in the country. The mixture, known on the streets as China White, TNT, or Poison, was gaining in popularity though it would be years before the CDC labeled these overdoses an epidemic. The combination of heroin and fentanyl, marketed in the illicit drug trade for its intense euphoria, had a dangerous lethality that few users then knew about.

The parents approached their daughter, breaking apart so that each could grasp one of her hands. The curly-haired father looked at me. I saw the question that formed in his eyes before he spoke.

"Did she suffer?" he said.

This was a familiar question, asked by next-of-kin, no matter what had caused the death—heart attack, car crash, hanging, gunshot wound. They asked at the scene or held onto it until we met in my office and discussed the autopsy report. Each loved one wanted to hear me say "No, they didn't suffer." Usually, the best I could offer was that it happened quickly.

In this case my reply should have been easy. No, she didn't suffer; she drifted off, went to sleep, never woke up. Opiates cause breathing to stop, affecting the respiratory center of the brain gradually until shutting it down completely. There is a gradual loss of consciousness.

"Did she suffer?" my friend repeated. Everyone waited for my reply.

"No," I said. "She didn't suffer."

Yet hadn't suffering compelled her to stick the needle in her arm and infuse the deadly cocktail?

My words felt like a lie.

The Trailer

The 12-year-old hurried up the two cement steps to the trailer, flipping the mountain bike on its side, front wheel still in motion. The screen door had barely enough life to creak shut.

"Hello?" he said, prepubescent voice cracking. In the quiet, he heard the numbers flipping to eight a.m. on the old General Electric clock.

In a long arc, his arm swept across the coffee table spilling ashtrays filled with cigarette butts, some stained with pink lipstick. Placing his backpack in the cleared space, he rifled through its contents until he found the red marker and looseleaf paper. Tears pooled at the corners of his eyes. He roughly wiped them away, leaving wet streaks through the dirt on his cheeks.

I saw this as if it were happening as I stood in the trailer and stared at his lifeless body hanging by a dog leash from the ceiling fan.

A forensic investigator snapped photos while I surveyed the 10-foot-wide mobile home. A single bedroom and bathroom were situated at the other end of the trailer. The living, dining, and kitchen areas were crammed together in this main part.

Rumpled clothing, dishes encrusted with bits of rice, pans with hardened grease, and empty two-liter soda bottles covered surfaces of counters, tables, and appliances. A naked twin mattress took up what little floor space was not occupied by other furniture. The bedding must have belonged to the boy.

The mother had found her son when she returned home from her day shift as an LPN at the hospital. She hoped to surprise him with his favorite dinner, pepperoni pizza. She had forgiven him for his transgressions.

Earlier that day while heading to work, she had seen the boy and his 13-year-old friend lolling in the park. Her son had told her he was headed to school. She could see he was goofing off. She stopped the car and confronted him. Her hand stung for several minutes after she slapped him. Yelling and swearing at him, she finished by grounding him for a month.

The pizza had been meant as a reconciliation. At the doorway, she dropped it onto the floor. The mess of pepperoni slices clumped together like a monstrous compound eye.

Neighbors heard the mother's howls. One called 9-1-1. Another came to her aid.

The investigator and I were alone with the body in the trailer. The cops had come and gone.

I examined the pre-teen's body, skin cool to the touch despite the warmth of the day. With eyes wide open and bulging, he looked afraid. His tongue protruded from his mouth, caught between clenched teeth, the tip dried. The skin above the noose was the color of a pale plum. His arms hung straight down at his sides. Shoulders slumped in dejection. Gravity gave his posture a hopeless air. His legs, bent at the knees, held him balanced on the coffee table. If he had stood up, he would have relieved the fatal pressure on his neck.

His face was turned away from the door, only the back of his head visible from the entrance. I felt grateful for this position. There was a chance his mother hadn't seen his face.

An uncapped pen and white, lined paper lay next to the backpack on the coffee table. One of the sheets had a torn edge. The boy's bare feet rested inches away. Red ink smeared the ends of his right thumb and index finger. He had written something. My eyes searched the room, but no suicide note appeared.

I patted down his stained white tee-shirt and reached into the pockets of his jeans. There I found a piece of ripped paper folded in half and then half again. The boy had tucked his message away in a secure location, not to be lost in the detritus.

My hands trembled as I unfolded it and read the messy block print: I HATE MY LIFE.

Part V

Life After…

I put down the scalpel for the pen.

The Visit

My job took me inside a prison whenever a fatality occurred there, investigating every time an inmate died. This occasion was different; it was personal. I was retired. The prisoner was alive.

On a cold autumn day, an hour drive from home, Marc and I sat in the parking lot staring at institutional architecture one story in height that looked like a public school circa the 1980s. The heavy-duty perimeter marked its purpose as a correctional facility. A brick guard tower loomed over us. The person on the observation deck must have a weapon, but with the interior shadowed, it couldn't be seen. Two rows of tall chain-link fence topped with razor wire fronted the tower.

Marc had driven, and he started to get out of the car.

"Wait," I said, checking my phone for the "Instructions for visitors." "We should leave our cellphones, money, and anything metal inside the car."

"We need our driver's licenses, right?" Marc said.

"Yes, of course. Just take it out of your wallet. Maybe we should put the stuff in the trunk, it won't all fit in here." I couldn't close the glove compartment.

"Good idea. I need my keys though."

We followed the signs to the intake area. No one else was in the waiting room. Two guards sat behind a counter talking to each other as we stood uncomfortably in front of them. After a few minutes, one of them waved us over.

We proffered our IDs and a guard handed us papers to fill out. At the bus-stop style benches, we noted the form required a DIN—the inmate number—for our friend. Luckily, I had memorized it, since it had been required on all correspondence I sent to the prison. Otherwise, we would have had to return to the car and my cellphone, which contained that information. Maybe the guards could have looked it up.

When we finished, the man clicked some keys on the computer and verified that we had a right to visit the prisoner. Presumably, he also checked whether we were felons, on parole, or had any outstanding warrants.

"You can rent a locker for your keys and such. See the list of things you can't bring in," the man said. He gave us our visitor's passes then turned back to his partner and resumed conversation. The only item we needed to secure were the car keys. The storage compartment dwarfed them.

Already I felt diminished. This medium-security world obscured life outside.

Marc and I left the small visitors' building and approached the main gate. As we got closer to the entrance, images of previous visits floated before me: windowless cells, solitary confinement, the smell of so many men in one place. I stopped walking. Taking my hand, my husband led me forward, past the ghosts.

Marc rang the outside intercom and explained our purpose. A loud buzzer sounded as the heavy metal gate slowly opened. We entered an outdoor vestibule and faced another barrier, while we waited for the first door to close behind us. I felt trapped between the two blockades and imagined them closing in on me, like in an Indiana Jones movie.

Another alarm shrilled in the air and the second metal gate crawled open. We traversed the 50-foot entry hallway to the next station where we were directed to a further series of checkpoints.

Finally, we reached the metal detector. We hadn't taken a chance with anything that might set it off. At home, we had dressed in clothing without any adornments: no belts, jewelry, or wedding rings. Anything else, we had left in the car.

As I approached, the guard pointed to my chest.

"You have to remove your bra," he said.

"Oh," I said, blushing, "there's no underwire." I had read that these thin metal strips in bras could set the detector off though I'd worn them often enough to courthouses and airports without a problem.

"Doesn't matter." He motioned me to get out of line.

I went to the single toilet room. Wads of paper speckled the floor; towels overflowed the trashcan. I fumbled to take off my bra trying not to put my shirt down on any surface. The mirror reflected the sagging remnants of nursing three sons.

What was the point of this procedure? Would the tiny clasps at the back of the bra set off an alarm? Did they do this to every woman entering? What nefarious thing could be obscured by the minute fasteners?

Controlling inmates wasn't enough; visitors were prisoners by extension.

I returned to the line; no cutting allowed. Already 30 minutes of visitation time had been used up in this slow admission process. I watched with humiliation as my bra went through the x-ray detector in a tray and then was handed back to me.

More visitors gathered, and we entered singly or in small family groups —again, through a double-lock system. An overseer, elevated for a good view of the room, supervised each person's entry. We gave him the slips of paper with our friend's name on it. He nodded to a specific table where we should wait. We sat in hardback chairs in the cafeteria-style space. I found another bathroom and replaced my bra.

As we waited for our friend, I felt inordinately nervous. Catholic School training had shaped me into a rule-follower. The nuns used rulers to smack boys' hands in the fifth grade; I have forgotten their offenses. If the teacher said, "Be quiet," I became a church mouse.

Imminent discipline hung in the atmosphere. I sat erect with my hands clasped on the table in front of me. Sitting sideways on the chair, putting hands off the desk, or not staring straight ahead might lead to a shout of "Guards, seize her." Did the inmates feel like this every minute of every day?

After seating everyone, the convicts were admitted. Our friend approached, looking thinner and more tentative than in his life outside these walls. The beige jumpsuit made his skin sallow. His broken glasses were taped in the middle and rested cockeyed on his nose. His face lit up when he saw us.

At first, the conversation lagged with stilted phrases: "How are you?" "How was the drive?"

We hadn't seen each other in about three years. Fury and betrayal had infused both Marc and me after the arrest and trial. We were angry with our friend for doing what he did—for using drugs, for running away, for becoming someone we didn't recognize. He wrote to Marc, expressed regret, and apologized. He asked us to visit. With reticence, I agreed to go with.

We bought snacks and drinks from the vending machine to temper the awkwardness. Small sandwiches were available, 1960s-automat style. As we sipped coffee, a rhythm developed to talk about life.

Our friend, an eternal optimist, told us of programs in which he was involved, classes he was taking, a newfound fitness and diet regimen. We told him of our family, what our sons were doing, and work.

He talked about regret for what he had done. The earnest admission showed as his eyes teared up. The pain clearly etched his face. I had the urge to take his hand or hug him.

"No touching," yelled the guard.

I hadn't even reached over. I glanced around.

Families reconnected around me. Partners talking to partners, mothers with sons, friends with friends. Their joy interrupted by disappointment at the oft-shouted rebuke.

The admonishment provided a segue to talk about where we were. I felt guilty even mentioning the intake process. After all, my friend's daily experiences eclipsed mine. Yet my surprise at being treated so rudely needed airing. We offered him sympathy as he began to share stories.

Only a few came out at that first visit, simple and benign ones. More came out in later conversations. The hardest tales didn't surface until after his release, some of the worst, in fact. I'm sure I still haven't heard them all.

Chairs scraped as people stood to say goodbye when the guard gave the 10-minute warning. Leaving happened more quickly than entering. What would our friend go through after visitation? Would he pass a metal detector? Would he need to strip down? Would he be cavity searched?

All the visitors filed out like a funeral procession. My mood remained unsettled as I passed through innumerable doors, had my identity checked, and trudged the long walkway to the final exit. I watched as people got on a weekly bus that came from the city (five hours away). Mothers with young children boarded; an entire day of travel for a few hours of proximity to a loved one.

The prison provided control for male felons, punishment for illegal behavior. Still, the dehumanization felt excessive as it rippled out to anyone connected with the prisoner. A cloak of shame had been laid across my shoulders.

The guard tower receded in the rear-view mirror. Quiet filled the car. The weight of the next five years of our friend's sentence rested heavily upon us.

Pen Pal

The business-sized envelope lay in the pile of daily mail: restaurant take-out flyers, real estate advertisements, and catalogs from McKenzie Childs and Vermont Country Store. I rarely received personal letters except from my cousin and my best friend. This semi-official letter wasn't from them.

The correspondence had my name typed on the front; the return address, a prison in central New York. It seemed like something I would have received as the Medical Examiner, but I'd been retired for years.

I didn't recognize the sender.

"Dear Dr. Jumbelic," it began. "I hope this letter finds you well."

There were several typed 8 ½-by-11-inch sheets, single sided, signed at the end by a man convicted of murder 14 years earlier. He had recently seen me on the television show *Dateline.*

He reminded me that we had previously corresponded. The man had been found guilty of murder. Another pathologist at the MEO had done the autopsy on the victim and testified at trial. The prisoner had admitted killing the victim, but swore it was self-defense. The prosecutors presented a case of premeditated and depraved conduct. When the verdict of guilty came in, the man felt wrongfully convicted.

He filed a lawsuit against my office, since it was the pathologist's testimony that had supported the theory of the prosecution. At the time, as the Chief ME, it would have been a conflict of interest for me to render my opinion, so I referred the files to the County Attorney and recommended they seek outside forensic expertise. The law department communicated with the prisoner.

In this letter, the prisoner asked for my professional opinion.

"I was intrigued watching you and seeing how you answered the difficult questions. I was on the edge of my bunk waiting for your next response," he wrote.

This man wanted me to review his case because he said that I "support the scientific truth and the forensic facts." He had been convicted of murder in the second degree, an intentional act that carried a life sentence. He maintained that his behavior was reckless, but he had no intent to kill, a crime considered manslaughter, which carried a lighter sentence, 15-25 years in jail.

He was seeking a reduction in the charges against him. To him, it was the difference between dying in prison and seeing life outside in his waning years. He had educated himself on the legal nuances of his crime, but he wasn't an attorney. He needed more than his part-time pro-bono lawyer to champion his case. Yet this wasn't suited for the Innocence Project or the ACLU. He wasn't a political prisoner or suffering any human rights abuse.

I wrote back.

Correspondence with an inmate was a slow process. In prison, there was limited access to paper, envelopes, pens, typewriters, and stamps. He labeled the letters "Legal Mail," so they were exempt from the added delay of official screening.

He gathered the evidence from the court and his former attorney. He sent me transcripts of the trial, autopsy reports, and x-rays. The material arrived in fits and starts: a thin letter promising more communication alternated with a thick bundle of records. He shared the contact information for his pro-bono lawyer.

The prisoner detailed the events from the day of the killing. He contended that he had defended himself against the victim. He disputed the story the prosecutors told at trial. The pathologist had backed up the state's opinion.

When I retired, I never had the desire for a forensic consulting business or to be a professional witness for hire. I had enough of courtrooms and depositions throughout my career. Still, even though officially out of the medical examining business, I hadn't lost my interest in solving a puzzle.

As Richard Feynman, the guru of quantum mechanics, said, "Once I get on a puzzle, I can't get off."

This prisoner wasn't the first to ask for my expert help on a personal matter. A friend of a friend asked for advice. A former colleague needed a professional opinion. A local attorney ran a case by me.

Someone's brother was missing and found in the river, could it be homicide? A man was killed in custody, could I explain that? A woman was found dead in bed. She was working on a delicate legal case. Was she murdered? A college student was found hanging in a tree, was he lynched? Were the official conclusions from the coroner or medical examiner, correct?

I reviewed the files—sifting data into categories, creating timelines, adding witness statements, looking at photos, police, and autopsy reports—all the work I did as an ME minus the corpses. I spoke to the next-of-kin and attorneys and gave them a forensic opinion. Most of the time, my findings supported the investigations the families were questioning. Either that or the result was inconclusive. Rarely had I uncovered a smoking gun.

After two years of communication with the prisoner, I had reviewed everything connected with the case—x-rays, autopsy reports and diagrams, toxicology tests, photographs, court transcripts—enough material to issue an expert opinion.

I contradicted the original pathologist. The prisoner was right.

COVID slowed the communication process even further. I hadn't heard from him in months. I feared the worst. The prisoner had extensive medical problems making him vulnerable to the virus. Then a letter arrived with the by-then-familiar return address. He had received my opinion.

"I hope this letter finds you well," he wrote at the start.

I appreciated these simple words of salutation. Someone on the inside wished someone on the outside well.

I write him back always hoping to find that he is well, too.

Prague

It had started from the tiniest of accidents, so small that were it not for the events that followed, completely forgettable. Marty had spent a summer in a Spanish immersion program. He would be a senior in high school in the fall. I met him in Europe, and we traveled to Scandinavia enjoying fjords, sculpture, and herring. Near the end of our journey, Marc joined us in Germany.

During the months preceding this trip, I felt the best I had in years since the diagnosis of rheumatoid arthritis forced my early retirement. After many different medications, I finally settled on a new biologic agent that lessened my joint pain and increased my mobility.

In Munich, we walked through Marionplatz admiring the architecture. The stones, broad and smooth, made a slippery surface when combined with discarded leaflets. My foot stepped on a paper, and I slid forward landing on my right knee and hand.

"Damn it," I said.

"What happened?" Marc said as he extended a hand to help me up.

"Stupid flyers," I said and began gathering them from the ground, embarrassed and irritable at the same time.

"You okay, Mom?" Marty said, checking my skin where it had struck the ground. "All good." There was no blood, bruise, or open wound.

"Let's go to dinner," I said. "*Das Bier* would be good."

This was our last night in Germany. We shared a festive meal with liter steins of beer, and plates of pork, cabbage, and potatoes. A photograph from that night shows me and my son smiling. My right hand holds a frothy mug. Much later I scrutinized this picture for any sign of the trouble that was about to begin. I still see none.

The next morning, we awoke at 5 a.m. to pick up a rental car to travel to Czechia. A dapper white Alfa Romeo awaited us. I told the guys to sit in the front. Feeling queasy, I settled in the back and put my head down.

Marc and Marty conversed and enjoyed the urban landscape and the tree-lined highways. If we broke any speed records on the Autobahn, I remained unaware. We stopped numerous times so I could use the roadside toilets. My body was on high alert with throbbing in my hand accompanied by gastrointestinal illness.

By the time we got to Prague, I needed a doctor. The hotel provided a list of local clinics.

"We'll have to walk," Marc said as the concierge circled locations on the map. The streets were narrow and congested with very little parking available. I moaned.

We headed to the cobblestoned and interlacing streets. The 95-degree heat and high humidity weighed us down as we tried first one and then another of the medical offices. Many businesses were closed for a church holiday. Finally, we met a physician who spoke English and had an x-ray machine. The pain had intensified. Marc thought my hand was broken.

The x-rays didn't show a fracture. The doctor splinted and wrapped my wrist anyway in case I had a sprain. The slightly red and swollen skin belied the intense gnawing I felt inside my hand.

No one took my temperature or checked my pulse and blood pressure.

After we left the clinic, we headed back to the hotel. I was hypotensive, had low blood sugar, and bacteria teemed in my blood. Although no one was aware.

"I'm going to die," I said.

My husband did not startle easily. My family thought I was being histrionic.

"Let's get you something to drink," Marc said. "Marty, sit on this stoop with Mom."

I bent my head forward; the sidewalk rippled below me. Marc went in search of bottled water, soda, or tea. He had no *Korunas*, Czech currency, but finally found a small bodega accepting credit cards and bought a Fanta.

When he returned with the orange soda, I cried. I had my heart set on Coca-Cola. As a child my mother had given me a teaspoon of the syrup when I suffered an upset stomach. The mirage of the familiar red and white logo faded as did my hope for survival.

Marc and Marty coaxed me and half-carried me back to the hotel. They reassured me my symptoms were due to the heat and dehydration. I lay down and insisted my family go to dinner. They didn't realize I could not lift myself up off the bed.

In the middle of the night, I awoke to my husband giving me a sponge bath. The splash of the cool water comforted my hot skin. Marc's face wavered over me.

"Hey, honey," he said when he saw my eyes open. "You were burning up." He refrained from telling me I had been unconscious. I had just enough strength to listen to Marc's voice.

Marc got me dressed and woke Marty up. My husband discussed tactics with the overnight desk clerk. Should he drive back to Munich knowing the stellar quality of German hospitals? Or were the hospitals here just as good? Would an ambulance come if he called? Could he drive me to the hospital? The young woman, in her early 20s, assured him Prague had the highest level of medical care but advised he call a cab. Marc and Marty carried me to the vehicle, explaining to the driver with gestures and broken phrases that I wasn't drunk or drugged, but needed a hospital. The private taxi rushed to the nearest emergency room. Marty stayed behind at the hotel. He hovered near maturity, close to 17.

My memory is like fragments of broken film restored by my family's telling of events.

Prague had a complicated medical network with urgent cases ferried to specific hospitals based on the presenting illness. One facility dealt with fractures and trauma, another with gastrointestinal problems, and another with emergency surgery; the buildings were spread all over the city.

We arrived at the Orthopedic unit. I had no bone problem. The next journey took us to the GI ward. My husband explained my symptoms with increasing franticness to the on-call doctor, who concluded I had traveler's diarrhea.

In a photo from that ER, I am lying on a steel gurney, like one of my patients, obtunded but not dead. My eyes are open and my face contracts with pain as I clutch my gauze-wrapped extremity to my lap, near my fecal-stained pants. Blood-soaked sheets cover a nearby stretcher devoid of its previous patient.

A nurse tried to take my blood pressure three times; changing the cuff, the machine and finally giving up, saying the equipment was broken. My blood pressure was so low it wouldn't register. It wasn't keeping my brain perfused.

I received no intravenous line, no fluids. No one came to clean me up. Precious time was lost in a very short window for treatment. The bacteria continued to multiply in my bloodstream with every beat of my heart.

My husband wept, powerless in a foreign system where his medical expertise was ignored; his life partner allowed to die. The attending doctor took our passports and ordered us to quarantine. I was transferred yet again, this time to an infectious disease hospital 30 minutes outside the city.

We arrived via ambulance at Bulovka in the early evening after 10 hours of non-treatment and less than 48 hours after my fall. I was unconscious; Marc was desperate.

A new doctor repeated questions asked by every previous physician —how long had I been ill? When did the vomiting and diarrhea start? What had I eaten in the last three days?

"Please just look at her hand, please," Marc said through tears. "No one has looked. She has an infection. A cellulitis. She's septic."

He had recognized the problem as soon as my fever spiraled out of control in the hotel room. He echoed what he told the other physicians: my history of an autoimmune disease treated with immunosuppression, my minor fall, the pain in my hand and low blood pressure.

"I'm a doctor." He had been repeating this mantra all day to no effect.

This physician paused, met his eyes, and then unwrapped the bandaging on my upper extremity, which hadn't been checked since its application. The swelling and reddening had increased. She quickly began to remove my clothing. Marc helped.

Large red blotches and blisters had spread on my chest: a telltale sign of *streptococcal* rash.

She fired orders in Czech interspersed with questions in English to my husband—Start a central line. When did this start? Antibiotics, run the IV wide open. Was there a skin wound? Give her cooling pads for the fever. When did she lose consciousness? Paracetamol for pain. How long has she been on Enbrel? Oxygen mask at two liters. Any other illnesses?

The pent-up story inside my husband flowed out as he answered. Hope infused him. This doctor and another, both infectious disease experts, worked on me every day for the next three weeks. Jana and Olga saved my hand and my life.

After being admitted to Bulovka hospital, I improved and temporarily woke up. Marc had gone back to the hotel to sleep.

The hospital room clouded around me; the oxygen mask suffocated me. I wanted it off. My hands didn't work properly. My right hand was completely bandaged and splinted. Trying to grip the complicated straps with my left hand, I only managed to slip the thing off my nose. The oxygen hissed against my nostrils.

A nurse saw the disturbed mask and readjusted it on my face, shaking a warning finger at me. She left the room. I called out with rusty vocal cords. The apparatus swallowed my words.

A second nurse, dressed in white, with a small cap on her head, reminded me of a protege of Florence Nightingale. She asked me unintelligible questions. Her words, clipped and guttural, sounded like a

Russian film dubbed in another foreign language. I remembered I was in Czechia.

The pain in my right hand felt as if I was being eaten from the inside out. The nickname for my infection was "flesh-eating bacteria."

Tears formed in the corners of my eyes. Her tone softened. She motioned for me to be calm, flattening her hands and making downward movements. I tried to inhale deeply and slowly. My lungs didn't cooperate.

Instead, my breaths came rapid, shallow, their timing automated by my brain's need for oxygen. The nurse patted my leg. I panicked that my body was going to do whatever it needed without my control. My respirations measured 40 per minute. I counted.

"This can't be good" flashed like a marquee beneath my closing eyelids, the last conscious thought before immersion into the terror of coma.

The virulent bacteria won that skirmish and shut down my lungs.

The next time Marc and Marty saw me, tubes and lines ran out of every orifice as well as my chest and arms, some sutured in place. A bag of yellow liquid hung on an IV pole on one side, a bag of clear solution on the other. Containers on the floor collected excess body fluids. Machines with multicolored numbers tracked my vital functions.

Marty followed those numbers assiduously and questioned every procedure.

"Dad, her pressure is up today," he said. "Her temperature is down." "Is that equipment for renal dialysis?" "Are they going to debride her arm again?"

He was the son of two physicians, wanting to study biology in college with the dream of becoming a doctor. He spent evenings in the hotel lobby, the only area with Wi-Fi, scouring the internet for articles on my diagnosis. He learned about the signs and symptoms, treatment, and the mortality statistics on necrotizing fasciitis and sepsis. He read papers on dealing with the loss of a parent. Later he told me he was convinced I would die.

In the pictures of myself in the ICU, I appear as a corpse, like those I examined for 25 years. My face and body are swollen and pale. My hand and arm, the source of the trouble, are swathed in gauze and beige bandaging. Fingers protrude from the end, swollen like mini kielbasas and about the same color.

The room is clean with large sunlit windows. An old-fashioned radiator sits against one side. The walls are tiled with beige squares, the floor light green linoleum. The white sheets with blue stripes down the center appear starched and without wrinkles.

One photo shows Marc in scrubs wearing a surgical mask and leaning toward me, eyes grim. He is holding my uninjured hand. His watch says 2 o'clock, the daily visiting time, the only hour of the day my family was allowed to see me. Another shows him kissing my forehead, saying goodbye.

The pictures with Marty remind me of when I viewed my dad in a casket. In my father's picture, he lays still, and his skin is chalky, like mine. I hate that photo.

My family tells me they discussed amputation, palliative care, and death. Joshua and David were marooned across the ocean at home in America while Marc and Marty saw me for an hour each day.

Throughout the eight days of my coma, consciousness floated beside me, and information seeped through a veil. I heard voices, dimly aware of my family's presence. Even in the haze I was aware of the drugs and treatment I received. The data were loose and tangled threads like a skein of wool. My brain spun the fragments into an elaborate tale.

In my dream state, I time-traveled to the assassination of Archduke Ferdinand, escaped the Germans in WWII, and had the US Navy Seals rescue me from a storage container docked in New York City. The physical space of that port locker looked eerily like my ICU room; as in real life, I was paralyzed in that nightmare. This cache of memories is more vivid than any nocturnal fantasy could be.

The waking up happened suddenly.

Doctors removed my breathing tube. My husband's face loomed over mine. He leaned closer, smiling and crying.

"Kill me," I said, my voice raspy from the intubation.

I tried to move my good hand to my face to dislodge the oxygen mask, but my limb was strapped down. I tried using my tongue to budge it.

"Kill me," I said.

Hearing what I thought was Russian spoken by the staff, I imagined being given a poisonous gas like Fentanyl that had been used in the Moscow Opera House siege. In my coma world, I had just survived an escape from imprisonment.

"These doctors saved your life, honey," Marc said calmly. He worried my brain had been damaged. He posted a sign next to my bed that read, "Everyone here is trying to help you," drew a heart, and signed his name. I trusted him.

The pain in my hand throbbed. Nurses fed me, washed me, and turned me. Every meal featured potatoes, their starchy aroma permeating the room. There was bitter tea for hydration, no potable water. I wanted to go home; I begged Marc to Medivac me to the United States.

"They're working on it," Marc said. "Maybe by Friday." That became Monday, then Wednesday. He placated me with an illusion of imminence. There could be no transfer in my unstable condition.

I gathered strength and moved from the ICU to a hospital room. My husband became my roommate, sleeping in the extra bed in the semi-private room. He shared breakfast and dinner with me and comforted me at night when I was in pain or scared. Marc went to the hospital cafeteria at lunch; they served beer. Marty had returned to the States to start his senior year of high school, reuniting with his older brothers.

Two weeks later, able to meet the requirement of transferring independently from chair to wheelchair, we flew home. We landed just before Rosh Hashana, the Jewish new year. It was especially sweet that year; the beginning of renewed life for me. Marc, Joshua, David, and Marty cared for me as I gathered strength from their presence and attention.

They took turns helping me shower and dress and eat. I learned how to walk again.

More surgery was needed to remove dead tissue and then I received a skin graft on my hand. By Thanksgiving, I didn't need the wheelchair. I could use both hands.

My doctors in Prague had saved me.

Facing Demons

Marc and I sat side by side in the backseat of a taxi. I stared out the window. The FEMA markings still stained the house fronts in New Orleans. It had been almost a decade since Katrina slammed into this Cajun town and nearly 10 years since I had first seen them.

During the searches, rescue workers spray painted an X on buildings after they completed their tasks indicating the date, team number, hazards and people found. The lowest digits sitting in the legs of the X were most familiar to me in my work. They represented the number of dead. A one over a two meant a single survivor and two deceased. My eyes sought the date. How long had the living person been confined with the corpses? I couldn't look away.

We had spent the morning traveling from New York to Louisiana. This was the last leg of the journey: Louis Armstrong Airport to our inn located in the Garden District. I had been looking forward to this trip, an ophthalmology conference for Marc and relaxation for me. I hadn't expected to confront my memories before I'd even stepped into the city.

"What's wrong?" Marc said as he saw me crying. His arm was over my upper back, and he squeezed my shoulder.

He had asked this question often enough in our 30 years of marriage. No answer was required. He knew the demons that haunted me, especially after 9-11. He had helped to exorcise them.

After working for three weeks at Ground Zero—examining body parts, calming firefighters, breathing in the smoke—I didn't return to New York City for four years. The thousands who had died were like an army holding the city in siege. I couldn't cross the barricade.

Then a cousin was getting married. It was to be a grand Russian affair in the Jewish tradition. Molly, Marc's cousin, was marrying Baba's son, Boris. Baba was my second mother; Boris, a half-brother. I did not want to miss this wedding.

Our entire family traveled to Manhattan. Excitement brimmed for the weekend's events as they settled into the hotel rooms. I felt edgy and fragile; the city, unfamiliar and uncomfortable.

"Come take a walk with me," Marc said.

I was reluctant. I could see the sun through the window sheers and the blue sky peeking between skyscrapers. We headed to the street. He pulled out a map he had gotten from the concierge. In the other hand he held a video recorder.

"I've got an idea," Marc said. "I'll interview you."

I hadn't anticipated this. I shook my head and turned around to go back.

"No, don't," he said. "I think this will be great for you to talk about your time here."

He knew the toll that working at Ground Zero had exacted on me—my sleepless nights, my abandonment of the city, the tears. It had taken two years to rid myself of the desire to cry every time I heard the national anthem, which was often since we had season tickets to Syracuse University basketball games. Bagpipes still brought profound melancholy.

Marc began to question me like a journalist interested in the details and recorded my answers. I haltingly talked about the rubble, the smoke, the bodies. Marc was struck by one story he remembered and asked me about it.

One day examining a severed arm, I saw that the watch on the deceased was identical to that on the wrist of the forensic anthropologist working with me. My colleague held the severed arm in such a way that the two watch faces were side by side. The crystals were almost touching —one working, one not, like the arms to which they were attached. I stared at the moving hand ticking the seconds as if the timepiece itself had a heartbeat.

We passed the gaping hole, awaiting construction of the World Trade Center memorial. Chain link fence surrounded the chasm. This space had been a mountain of debris when I last saw it. We stood at the side, transfixed by the enormity of the destruction.

Heading down Vesey Street, I saw a crack in the sidewalk and halted. I remembered this distinct fissure. It had been steps away from my post at the temporary morgue and I passed it multiple times a day.

I wept. The camcorder whirred on.

In the months and years that followed, Marc and I resumed our trips to the Big Apple. Joshua lived in New York for 5 years. It was more than 20 years before I toured the Memorial. I have never watched Marc's homemade video.

My reaction in New Orleans surprised me. Perhaps because I had gotten past my feelings in NYC enough to visit and have fun, or because I had spent most of my time during Katrina 65 miles away at the morgue in St. Gabriel, or maybe because so much time had passed.

As we rode in the taxi past the houses marked by FEMA, I envisioned the wet and mud and smelled the muck and decay. Hundreds of dead recovered from this city. Many were elderly and poor. Some wore hospital bands, others janitorial uniforms. They drowned or suffered blunt trauma. They died of heat exposure or lack of water. They had heart attacks or succumbed to diabetes or emphysema. Some had wounds that festered into sepsis. A few were murdered or took their own lives.

As we passed the convention center, I saw the ghost of a woman down on her knees gesturing for help. The news media captured that despair three days after the hurricane made landfall. Who did she lose? Had they been on my autopsy table?

The devastated Ninth Ward shimmered through the taxi's passenger window. I saw the mirage of the tops of buildings peeking out of the flood waters with folks huddled on roofs along with handmade messages "PLEASE HELP US. 5 people. 1 cat. 1 dog."

Finally arriving at the quaint bed and breakfast, I relaxed into the soft mattress only to be reminded of the military cot beneath me where I had slept for two weeks as I worked for the federal government identifying the dead.

I closed my eyes and conjured remembrances of happier times. As a young couple, Marc and I had strolled through the French Quarter marveling at the elaborate architecture, all manner of musical instruments accompanying us. We heard trombones, fiddles, and the percussion of 5-gallon buckets. We discovered the cocktail 'Hurricane' at O'Brien's Pub and bought souvenirs of the tall glasses, which sit in our breakfront at home.

For this trip, I hoped to see the decorations and floats at a museum called Mardi Gras World. I looked forward to tasting the familiar jambalaya, gumbo, crawfish etouffee, and oysters. I longed for the beauty and peace of St. Louis Cathedral and Jackson Square. I drifted off to sleep.

When I awoke it was late afternoon.

"You must have needed that nap," Marc said. He was sitting in an overstuffed chair reading the daily *Times-Picayune*. "Want to go for a beignet and a cup of Cafe du Monde?"

"Think we can get one at this time of day?" I said.

"Sure," he said and reached out his hand to pull me up.

DEATH CALLING

Brrring. Brrring. Brrring.

"I got it," I shouted, racing down the stairs from my bedroom.

The sound resonated through the Baltimore row house. Each ring bloomed with hope. I heard the scrape of my mother's chair on the linoleum floor in the kitchen. Hurrying my pace, I took the stairs two at a time and swung on the newel. My hand reached for the receiver as Mom appeared in the doorway. My 13-year-old enthusiasm outpaced her.

"Hello?" I said, grasping the receiver in both hands. My breath came rapid fire.

"Mar?" my friend said.

"Who is it?" Mom asked.

"It's Irene," I said.

"Didn't you just see her all day in school?"

"That doesn't count. We didn't get to really talk. Besides, I won't be long. Her mom only lets her on the phone for 15 minutes."

"Well, good." My mom went back to reading *Reader's Digest.*

On the phone, Irene and I dissected every look from a boy, each comment from a teacher, any piece of gossip from friends. We were in junior high. This nightly talk was as essential to us as eating or sleeping.

Brrring. Brrring. Brrring.

It was the classic sound of a ringing rotary phone. Decades later, long after junior high, college, and medical school, I was in my own house in the suburbs in Central New York with three sons of my own. The telephone, still essential to me, had transformed into a purveyor of doom, especially in the middle of the night.

The fifth ring woke me from my sleep.

On the other end of the line was BATO's familiar voice. "I know you're not on call, but I thought you should know about this one."

The clock radio read 3:00 a.m. I forced myself to sit up. My husband snored beside me. No sound came from the boys' bedrooms. I longed to slip back to my dream—swimming in warm Caribbean waters.

"Are you there, Dr. J?" he said.

"Talk to me."

"Four college students dead in a single car accident. Maybe one other injured. I don't have those details yet."

I watched the ceiling fan spin—cycling round and round like the tires on the overturned vehicle. My husband rolled over and pulled the blankets tighter around him, unaware of Death's intrusion. I picked up my penlight, notepad, and pen.

"What's the address?"

"I'll pick you up in the jeep. It's out your way."

"Thanks." I frequently drove to scenes at night by myself. BATO's offer to accompany me felt welcome.

Somewhere in town, I imagined other phones ringing. Police informing the next-of-kin about the demise of their loved one.

A mother dropping to her knees intoning her child's name.

A father asking over and over, "How do you know it's him?"

A roommate remarking, "But I just talked to her a few hours ago."

One telephone going unanswered.

Calls that changed lives into before and after segments.

Moonlight drifted through the window slats. Dust motes pirouetted. I got up and changed into work clothes. I made a cup of coffee, the first of many needed that day, grateful for this routine pleasure.

My gear and I waited on the front porch, so my investigator wouldn't need to call when he arrived. The phone would not ring again that night.

Brrring. Brrring. Brrring.

The same classic tone yet foreign in this modern age. It startled me as I waited for the barista to serve up my cappuccino. I imagined hearing my name, Dr. Jumbelic, in a phantom handset. A fellow customer reached into his jacket pocket and answered his mobile. Words of happy conversation ensued. Relief displaced my concern—Death wasn't calling. He hadn't called me in a long time. I had retired ten years earlier.

Irritation followed.

This reverberation from the past was a reminder of my tete-a-tetes with Death. I heard this classic ring much less frequently of late. It had morphed to beeps, whistles, strains of ABBA, Bach, or the *Twilight Zone* theme, and thousands of customizable melodies. Still for some, the retro melody held nostalgic appeal.

Yet after so many years as a medical examiner, Death had stolen the formerly friendly sound of my youth for his malevolent announcements. I imagined his voice, a whisper in my ear.

"Mary," the barista called and handed me my cup.

I inhaled the beloved scent deep into my lungs. I headed to the library, where quiet would surround and the familiar smell of books would comfort me.

No phones allowed.

In the Kitchen

The stainless steel of the refrigerator door felt cool against my forehead. My heart hammered. My throat seized up. I tried to quiet my sobs as my breath came in staccato bursts. My eyes squeezed shut.

Marty, a man of 25, turned on the light in the kitchen.

"Mom, what's wrong?" my son said.

I turned to him; tears spilled down my cheeks. He looked like he had just finished working out—dressed in a sleeveless t-shirt and running shorts, his hair plastered to his forehead.

"I just can't go on a ventilator again," I said. "Please let me die at home."

Spring of 2020 had arrived in New York with a tsunami of COVID. Joshua and Marty returned to the family home to quarantine. David already lived in town, in an apartment nearby with his girlfriend, Kelsey. We could only visit with him through the glass doors to the porch and watch each other cry.

Marty approached and put his arms around me, pulling my head to his chest. When he was six years old, he barely reached my elbow. I called him my little peanut. He grew and I shrunk. My tears wet his shirt.

"I know, Mom, I was there," he said.

It had happened eight years earlier. One second, I was breathing, and the next I wasn't. Terror had filled me as I counted my own respirations right before they stopped. A cytokine and toxic storm (like the effects of Coronavirus) had swept through my body. Without sophisticated medical intervention, I would have died. Even with it, the outcome had been far from certain.

There had been no glorious white light or heavenly chorus, no cherubim to welcome me through the pearly gates, only darkness and unending night. My coma hadn't been a romantic slumber. My oblivion was a hellish nightmare. I did not want to re-enter that purgatory.

"It's going to be okay, Mom. We're all home and being safe," Marty said.

I didn't feel that. No one knew how the coronavirus was spread—aerosol or fomites? Was it safe to go to the store? To receive mail? Why did the CDC say masks don't help? In my job I had worn N-95s all the time. They protected me from inhaling dangerous pathogens. Why should that be any different with this virus?

During my prior hospitalization, Marty had found comfort in data. By following the ups and downs of the machines, he interpreted whether I was doing better or worse. As we stood there next to the refrigerator, he reminded me how I defied the mortality figures back then. Ninety percent of people in the same circumstances died. I had survived.

"You're indestructible," Marty said.

We glanced over as Joshua plodded to the kitchen for a snack. He had been reading a text message on his phone but upon seeing Marty and me, immediately set it down on the counter. Without speaking, Joshua joined the hug. He relied on mindfulness for calm, an awareness of the moment. The three of us gathered in embrace. My sons infused me with their strength. Our breathing synchronized.

The aroma of coconut from Joshua's recently shampooed hair enveloped me. I took in the sweet tang of Marty's sweat. My heart rate slowed. I swallowed tears. Warmth emanated from their skin in a rejuvenating aura. I held onto my sons.

Uncertainty swirled in the world outside; confidence collected inside. If my next breath was my last, this love would be enough.

Pandemic

My family loves board games. There is a plethora to choose from in our closet: strategy, engine building, competitive, cooperative, two to six players, with quick or evening-length play times. The childhood familiars are there too—a Spanish version of Monopoly that Marc and I picked up on a vacation to Mexico before we had children, and a tattered box of Risk, the source of many a turned-over gameboard when the older two boys were little.

In the era of COVID, one stands out—*Pandemic.*

In the game, players take the roles of specialists working together to eradicate dangerous infectious diseases on a world map. Matt Leacock published the game in 2008 but it is apropos for this real-life global situation. The medical theme feels especially well-suited to my family. We gravitate to it—an opportunity to beat the virus, at least in fantasy.

My family sets the game board up on the kitchen table. Red, blue, yellow, and black cubes of disease dot cities around the globe. If we really want a challenge, we play with the purple virulent strain cubes.

At the beginning of the game, there are nine infected cities around the globe. Each player takes the role of an expert with more than a dozen to choose from including dispatcher, operations expert, contingency planner, scientist, and epidemiologist. We travel to sites of infection, build research stations, produce vaccines, and set up quarantines. We work diligently to anticipate the next action of the virus and try to cure the disease, even better if we can eradicate it.

A pattern has emerged. A feeling of collective optimism arises halfway through. Maybe we contained the disease on two continents and eliminated one strain. Overconfident, I check my watch to plan the rest of the evening. We are on schedule to finish in the usual 45 minutes.

The threat starts small—a cured disease recurs in a remote town. The infection spreads and reasserts itself in an urban center or a superbug appears in Delhi. Perhaps a mutation pops up in Milan. My player, this time a medic, is stuck in North America when an epidemic hits Lagos in Africa. Within a few turns, the outbreak hits Riyadh. We race to distribute vaccines.

We discuss strategy, reminiscent of governmental table-top exercises I participated in throughout my career. I worked with local, state, and federal agencies to plan for future occurrences of the 1918 influenza or H5N1. When we play the game, I apply this professional experience as my family tries to save the world from overwhelming disease.

We encounter explosive results as countries, then continents are swept by an indefensible wave of infection. Our hubris on conquering the virus is short-lived. The opponent is always ahead of us. Even when we ultimately win, we teeter on the precipice of losing.

We track our wins and losses on the inside of the box top. Right now, we are at 50/50 after close to 100 matches.

Disease and death have always surrounded me. Control is an illusion.

Life is not over until it's over and it's not over yet.

THE END

About the Author

Mary Jumbelic, M.D., is a board-certified forensic pathologist who performed thousands of autopsies during her 25-year career. She received awards for her work from the National Transportation Safety Board and the New York State Senate, and has been recognized by the National Organization of Women as a trailblazer. In retirement, she has published many nonfiction stories, accounts of her life both in and out of the morgue. This is her first book. She lives with her husband in Central New York.

She speaks for the dead.
They speak for her.

MARYJUMBELIC.COM
Final Words Publishing